ADVENTURE GAMES BOOK

The Sinister
Lake Game

based on Enid Blyton's
Five on a Hike Together

Illustrated by Gary Rees

HODDER AND STOUGHTON
LONDON SYDNEY AUCKLAND TORONTO

British Library Cataloguing in Publication Data

The Sinister Lake game.– (Famous Five adventure games)
   1. Games– Juvenile literature   2. Adventure and
adventurers– Juvenile literature
I. Series
793'.9   GV1203

   ISBN 0-340-36400-9

First published 1985
Fourth impression 1988

Published by Hodder and Stoughton Children's Books,
a division of Hodder and Stoughton Ltd,
Mill Road, Dunton Green, Sevenoaks, Kent TN13 2YJ

Photoset by Rowland Phototypesetting Ltd,
Bury St Edmunds, Suffolk

Printed in Great Britain by Hazell, Watson & Viney Ltd,
Member of BPCC plc,
Aylesbury, Bucks

You have often read about The Famous Five's adventures . . . now here's your chance to take part in one!

This time YOU are in charge. YOU have to work out the clues, read the maps, crack the codes. Whether The Five solve the mystery or not is in your hands.

You will not necessarily solve the mystery on your first attempt. It may well take several goes. Keep trying, though, and you will eventually be successful.

Even when you *have* solved the mystery, the game can still be played again. For there are many different routes to the solution – and each route involves different clues and adventures.

So the game can be played over and over. As many times as you like!

HOW TO PLAY

To solve the mystery, you have to go with The Five on an adventure through the book. You do this by starting at PARAGRAPH ONE and then following the instructions to other paragraphs.

Many of the paragraphs will ask you to work out some sort of clue. You do not have to work out every one of the clues to solve the final mystery . . . but the more you manage, the more you're likely to be successful. The less clues you crack, the less chance of completing the adventure.

To help you work out the clues, there are several pieces of equipment available – a map, a measuring tape, a pair of binoculars and a codebook. You can start with only *one* of these EQUIP-MENT CARDS but you will often pick up others as the game goes along. Occasionally, however, you will be asked to give some up as well.

To hold your EQUIPMENT CARDS during the adventure, there is a RUCKSACK CARD. This will tell you exactly which EQUIPMENT CARDS you have for use at any one time (so, after they've helped in solving a clue, always remember to return them to your rucksack). Any EQUIPMENT CARDS not in your rucksack **cannot be used or consulted** – and therefore should be kept out of play.

Of course, no Famous Five adventure could take place without provisions. You are therefore given three PICNIC CARDS. These are to be kept in the slit of the LUNCHBOX CARD.

Every time The Five eat or lose some of their provisions during the adventure, you must remove one of your PICNIC CARDS from the LUNCHBOX CARD. When there are no PICNIC CARDS left in your LUNCHBOX, the provisions have run out and so you cannot possibly continue with the adventure. The game is over and you will have to start again from the beginning.

READY TO START

The Famous Five are JULIAN (the biggest and eldest), DICK, GEORGE (real name Georgina, but she always wanted to be a boy), ANNE and George's dog, TIMMY.

It is their half-term holiday and they have gone for a hike across the countryside. They intend to spend their first night at a cosy little farmhouse but, on the way, Timmy falls down a hole and bruises his leg. Julian and George therefore take him into the nearest village to find a vet, while Dick and Anne head for the farmhouse on their own. Someone misdirects them, however, and Dick and Anne knock on the wrong door.

The house is owned by an old woman called Mrs Taggart. She says they must go away before her bad-tempered son comes back but she eventually agrees to let them stay. As long as they keep well out of sight, that is . . . So Anne is given a bed in the loft while Dick has to make do with sleeping in the barn.

In the middle of the night, Dick is suddenly woken up by a voice from outside. The mysterious caller then slips a message to him through the window. On meeting up with Julian and George again the following morning, Dick recounts this strange incident. To begin with, the others think he has just dreamt it, but then he shows them the message he received. It has something to do with stolen jewels and tells how they are hidden at a place called Sinister Lake.

This all seems very puzzling but then Julian suddenly thinks he knows what has happened. There had just been an escape from the nearby prison and it was probably the escaped prisoner who had called at the barn. He must have arranged to meet someone there and mistakenly thought Dick was that person. The message was probably to tell the other person where to find the spoils from a past burglary of his in case the prisoner was caught again before he could reach them himself.

The Five go and tell all this to the local police but the police think they are just letting their imaginations run away with them. There seems only one thing for them to do; go in search of Sinister Lake and the hidden jewels themselves . . .

To join them on this search, you will first of all need to put on your rucksack. So pick out the RUCKSACK CARD and have it near to you. You must now choose a piece of equipment to take with you. The Five each have a map, a measuring tape, a pair of binoculars and a codebook – but you can start with only *one* of these. Which do you think would be the most useful? Insert the EQUIPMENT CARD you have chosen into the slit of your RUCKSACK CARD and keep the remaining three EQUIPMENT CARDS out of play until told you can pick them up.

Now for the provisions. A kindly bread-shop owner has prepared The Five a delicious picnic of sandwiches, cherry cake and ginger beer. Put the three PICNIC CARDS into the slit of your LUNCHBOX CARD. Don't forget to remove a picnic card every time The Five eat or lose some of their provisions.

Remember: when there are no PICNIC CARDS left in your LUNCHBOX, the adventure has to stop and you must start the game all over again.

Good Luck!

'Do you think Timmy's leg will have healed sufficiently yet?' Anne asked, knowing that there might well be a lot of walking to be done. George let him run round the village green for a bit just to check. 'Yes, it seems about as good as new!' she laughed with relief as he bounded across the grass. Now that they were sure Timmy was fit enough – for they couldn't possibly have gone without him! – they prepared to set off for Sinister Lake. 'We'd better ask someone if they can tell us roughly which direction to go,' suggested Julian. But who should they ask? Julian had one idea, while Dick had another. In fact, every one of them seemed to have a different idea – even Timmy! 'We're going to have to come to some sort of agreement,' chuckled Dick, 'or we'll be asking the whole village!'

Throw the special FAMOUS FIVE DICE to decide whose idea they should accept – then turn to the appropriate number. If you throw 'Mystery', you must turn to that number instead.

JULIAN thrown   go to 231
DICK thrown   go to 181
GEORGE thrown   go to 61
ANNE thrown   go to 33
TIMMY thrown   go to 47
MYSTERY thrown   go to 87

'. . . ninety-eight paces, ninety-nine paces, one hundred!' they counted – and there the little turning was, exactly as the sergeant had said. They were just about to set off down the turning when the sergeant came running after them. 'Here, take this map with you,' he said, 'I don't want you all getting lost. The countryside round here can be quite desolate in parts.' Julian told him that they each had a map already but the sergeant explained that this was a special police map with more detail. So they agreed to take it with them, saying goodbye to him again.

If you don't already have it, put the MAP CARD into your RUCKSACK. Now go to 111.

They hadn't followed Dick far along the river bank when Timmy sniffed out a tobacco tin amongst the grass. Opening it up, they found that there was a sheet of paper inside with some sort of drawing on it. 'I wonder what all these arrows mean,' said George, thinking that it looked a bit like the plan of a castle. Julian then noticed that the underneath of the tin had some writing scratched on to it. Unfortunately, it seemed to be in code, and so he suggested taking out their codebooks to see if they could help.

Use your CODEBOOK CARD to find out what the message said by decoding the instruction below. If you don't have one, go to 249 instead.

4

'This must be it!' said George when, exactly on pace 140, they reached a little gap in the hedge. Squeezing through, they found themselves at the beginning of a rough path across some empty fields. 'I suppose we just keep following it until we reach a signpost or something,' said Julian as he led the way. **Go to 224.**

5

Having found the windmill on their maps, they then started walking in the direction that they had seen the lake. 'No wonder they call it Sinister Lake,' remarked Dick, remembering how dark and eerie it had looked from the windmill. 'It gave me the creeps even from all those miles away!' The others agreed, only hoping it wouldn't look so bad when they were actually there. **Go to 163.**

6

'I'm afraid my suggestion wasn't such a good one after all!' Dick apologised when they had been following him for well over half an hour and still hadn't passed anything they recognised. It was at that moment that George spotted a huge tree to their left. 'Gosh, I've never seen such a big tree,' she exclaimed, 'and – look – there's some sort of fence around it!' Going closer, they saw that there was also a notice at the bottom which said that the tree was the largest one in the area. 'If it's that important,' said Anne, 'then it will probably be shown on our maps.' So she suggested they look it up to find out roughly where they were.

Use your MAP CARD to find which square the fenced tree is

17

They had still to reach the bridge when Dick noticed a wooden table and some seats at the side of the road. 'It must be a picnic place,' he said, and it looked so inviting that he suggested stopping there for a short while themselves. 'Mm, what delicious country bread!' exclaimed George as she munched on one of her sandwiches. She wasn't the only one to think so, though, because the little table was soon covered with hundreds of sparrows! 'We'd better continue towards the bridge,' said Julian, quickly closing his lunchbox up again, 'or they're going to eat every crumb we have!'

Take one PICNIC CARD from your LUNCHBOX. Now go to 136.

18

Just at that moment they heard someone come running up behind them. Turning round, they saw it was a jogger and Julian decided it was about time to ask the way again. 'You're looking for Sinister Lake,' said the jogger, running on the spot so he wouldn't have to stop. 'You should have taken the little turning across the fields 140 paces back down this lane. I know it's that number because I run this same route every day!' As soon as he was gone, the children started to count the 140 paces.

Use your MEASURE CARD to count the 140 paces yourself – then follow the instruction there. If you don't have one in your RUCKSACK, you'll have to guess which instruction to follow.

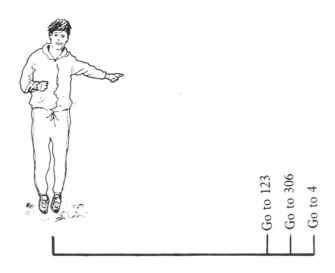

Go to 123
Go to 306
Go to 4

19

'Perhaps we ought to ask the way again,' said Julian when they had walked quite a bit further along the river-bank. 'We might have to leave the river soon and take a path across the fields or something.' But the trouble was there was no one to ask – not a soul in sight! Just before the next bend, however, there was a tall tree and Dick suggested that he climb it to see if the lake was visible from up there. He carried his binoculars with him to make it easier and when he was nearly at the top he steadied himself against a branch while he looked through them.

Use your BINOCULARS CARD to try and spot the lake by

placing exactly over the shape below – then follow the instruction. If you don't have one in your RUCKSACK, go to 213 instead.

```
        G R Z O M H N T L S    S    T    E       O
  T W       H    O K R   N    E ! R         E
    T  E IG  H R     O T  W  J& E     O P  E
  ⅞ O    S   Z    E     N    V    E    E  ? C  N  Y
```

20

'We must be *here*,' said Julian, finding a castle on his map. 'So that means we need to go in an easterly direction – towards that dip over there!' On the way, they discussed Mrs Taggart's horrible son and why he should have deliberately misdirected them. 'I just can't understand it,' said Julian. 'It's not as if we are doing *him* any harm by going to Sinister Lake!' ***Go to 90.***

21

'Come on – if I can do it, so can you!' George boasted when she had landed on the other side of the brook. So the others wasted no time in jumping it themselves – first Julian, then Anne, then Timmy and last of all Dick. They were just about to leave the brook when Dick noticed a bottle in the water. 'Look, there's a piece of paper inside!' he exclaimed and he rolled up his sleeves to try and reach it. He was at last just able to get hold of it and he lifted it up on to the bank. When they pulled the piece of paper out, they found that there was a message inside! *TO REACH SINISTER LAKE* . . . it began, but the rest was in some sort of code. 'Quick, our codebooks!' Julian said excitedly as he started to unzip his rucksack.

Use your CODEBOOK CARD to find out what the message said by decoding the instruction below. If you don't have one, go to 126 instead.

22

Measuring fifty metres from the stepping-stone, they came to a small hole in the ground. 'It looks like an old rabbit burrow,' said Julian and, sure that rabbits weren't still using it, he put his hand in. 'There's something there!' he said excitedly and his fingers managed to pull out a small, tatty book. It wasn't just any old book, though. Opening it, they saw that it was full of secret codes!

If you don't already have it, put the CODEBOOK CARD into your RUCKSACK. Now go to 91.

The coded message said that they were to beware of the nineteenth stepping-stone since it would start to sink at the slightest touch. As they carefully jumped from the eighteenth to twentieth stone, they wondered why the message hadn't been written in plain English since it was so important. Then it suddenly dawned on Julian! He told them that the stepping-stone was probably set as a trap by that prisoner when he had originally come to hide the jewels and was to stop people going too close to the lake. The coded warning was probably so his accomplices would know about it. 'Well, it's a good job we had the same type of codebooks ourselves!' said George, as they finally reached the end of the stepping-stones. *Go to 91.*

'It looks like we're entering some sort of wood,' said Dick when they had done quite a bit more walking. This was the only wood they had seen in the area and so Julian said they should have no trouble finding it on their maps. They would then be able to tell how much further they had to go!

Use your MAP CARD to find which square the wood is in – then follow the instruction. If you don't have one, you'll have to guess which instruction to follow.

If you think D4	go to 176
If you think E3	go to 39
If you think E4	go to 53

George suddenly thought this would be a good opportunity to prove how brave she was, however, and surprisingly went into the house first! 'My shiver was just because there was a bit of a breeze,' she explained casually. But she made sure Timmy was right behind her as she moved amongst the dark shapes of furniture! They came to a part of the floor that was lit up a little by a shaft of light from a broken window. 'Look, that floorboard's got some writing on it!' Julian suddenly exclaimed, pointing to a message in yellow chalk. They all bent nearer so they could see what it said. *BEWARE HOLE IN FLOOR 40 METRES FURTHER ALONG*, they all read together. Since they probably wouldn't be able to see it in this dark, they decided they had better use one of their measuring tapes.

Use your *MEASURE CARD* to measure this 40 metres – then follow the instruction there. If you don't have one, you'll have to guess which instruction to follow.

Go to 186

Go to 140

Go to 226

26

'I hope there aren't any rats down here!' said Dick as they started to count the forty paces. 'I hope there aren't too many cobwebs either!' Anne said, putting her hand to her face. At least, there was Timmy to protect them from rats! *Go to 55.*

27

They were just about to decode the message when something extraordinary happened. It suddenly started to disappear! 'It must have been written in a special ink that gradually vanishes!' said Julian, desperately trying to remember some of it. But it was too late – it had now completely gone! 'Never mind,' said Dick, 'at least we learnt something from those people. If they're going to *dive* for the jewels, it must mean they're in the lake somewhere!' Before they returned to the lake, however, they decided to have some of their picnic just inside the house. All these adventures were making them hungry.

Take one PICNIC CARD from your LUNCHBOX. Now go to 157. (Remember: when there are no more picnic cards left in your lunchbox, the game is over and you must start again.)

They hadn't followed George far round the edge of the lake when they came to a small sign. It read *NO FISHING WITHOUT PERMIT*, but over the top someone had scribbled something else. They all bent down to have a closer look. *WALK 80 METRES TOWARDS THE SILVER BIRCH*, it read. Looking round, they suddenly spotted a silver birch back in the direction of the house and, since there seemed to be no others, they assumed it must be that! All they had to do now was take out their measuring tapes!

Use your MEASURE CARD to measure the 80 metres from the sign – then follow the instruction there. If you don't have one, you'll have to guess which instruction to follow.

Go to 239

Go to 209

Go to 70

While they were still discussing whose suggestion to follow, they suddenly heard the distant sound of a train beyond the trees. 'That must be on the line that runs through the village!' Dick suddenly realised. 'Quick – let's see if we can spot it, then we'll know where the line is!' So he hurriedly led the way through the trees, soon coming out on to the moorland again. 'Can you see it anywhere?' Dick asked anxiously as they peered all round for the train. Unfortunately they couldn't, so George quickly looked for her binoculars to see if they would help.

Use your BINOCULARS CARD to try and spot the train by placing exactly over the shape below – then follow the instruction. If you don't have one, go to 317 instead.

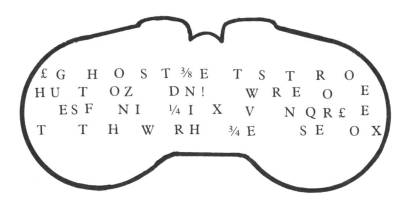

£ G   H   O   S   T ⅜ E   T   S   T   R   O
HU   T   O Z   D N !   W   R E   O   E
   E S F   N I   ¼ I   X   V   N Q R £   E
T   T   H   W   R H   ¾ E   S E   O   X

Anne's map *did* have the marshland on it and it showed that there was a small river nearby that ran all the way to the outskirts of the village. 'It must be that down there!' said George, pointing to a thin strip of water that twisted through the fields. They hadn't been following the river far when Timmy discovered a pair of binoculars amongst the reeds at the edge. George decided to put them in her rucksack so she could hand them in at the police station, but the others told her to hurry up about it since the daylight was beginning to fade already!

If you don't already have it, put the BINOCULARS CARD into your RUCKSACK. Now go to 59.

31

They suddenly realised there was a problem, however. How were they going to keep one end of the measure by the float? Normally, one of them would stand there with it but it was going to be a bit difficult in water! So they decided they would just have to guess the sixty metres. 'At least we know which direction to go,' said Julian as he paddled the raft towards the tall tree. Suddenly, though, Anne shouted at them to stop. 'Look, there's a sunken rowing-boat down there!' she exclaimed, pointing into the murky water. 'And I can just make out a red polythene bag inside. It must be the jewels!' To celebrate, George handed round her ginger beer!

Take one PICNIC CARD from your LUNCHBOX. Now go to 240. (Remember: when there are no picnic cards left in your lunchbox, the game is over and you must start again.)

32

'It's a good job we've got this helicopter with us,' the sergeant told them as they hurried across the yard at the back to where it was waiting. 'Normally, a village police station wouldn't have one but we've been lent it for the day to hunt down that escaped prisoner!' The Five all ducked their heads to avoid the whirling propeller and then started to climb into the helicopter. 'One of you had better sit at the front with the pilot to help direct him,' said the sergeant as he helped them up.

Throw the FAMOUS FIVE DICE to decide who it's to be.

JULIAN thrown	go to 272
DICK thrown	go to 147
GEORGE thrown	go to 202
ANNE thrown	go to 60
TIMMY thrown	go to 16
MYSTERY thrown	go to 241

33

They all finally decided that Anne's idea sounded best – to call in at the village post-office and ask there. 'Are you sure you want to go to Sinister Lake?' the postmaster asked dubiously when they had walked up to his counter. 'There are a lot of bad stories about the place.' He could see that they weren't to be put off, though, and so he finally agreed to direct them. 'Keep walking out of the village until you reach a bridge,' he told them, 'then follow the river downstream. That will point you in roughly the right direction.' On the way, Julian suggested looking up the bridge on their maps to find out how much further it was.

Use your MAP CARD to find which square the bridge is in – then follow the instruction. (Remember to put it back in your RUCKSACK afterwards.) If you don't have a MAP in your RUCKSACK, you'll have to guess which instruction to follow.

If you think D1	go to 122
If you think C1	go to 17
If you think E1	go to 160

34

Julian said that the signpost would be too far to read even *with* the binoculars, however, and there was nothing for it but to go a lot closer. Anne was so impatient to see if she had been right or not that she virtually ran all the way. 'Yes, it does point to the lake!' she called back delightedly to the others. 'It says that it's another four miles!' ***Go to 224.***

35

When they reached a hundred paces, they searched all round but there were no binoculars to be seen. 'Perhaps it meant a hundred paces the other way,' suggested George. 'Or even a hundred paces wading across the river!' added Dick. Whatever it meant, they didn't have all day and so they decided just to continue on their journey. 'What a shame, though,' sighed Julian. 'A spare pair of binoculars might well have been useful!' He knew from previous adventures how easily they could get lost or broken! ***Go to 19.***

36

When they reached the old windmill, they immediately started walking round it to look for an entrance. 'Look, here it is!' Dick shouted, finding a small wooden door. Stepping through, they were soon climbing the rickety stairs to the top. George noticed a window in the far corner and they all went over to it, staring across the countryside below for signs of the lake. 'That must be it!' said Julian excitedly as he pointed to a large tree-sheltered pool in the far distance. Remembering which direction it was, they quickly returned to the bottom and the open air again. Before they left the windmill, however, Julian suggested looking it up on their maps, so they would know where they were.

Use your MAP CARD to find which square the windmill is in – then follow the instruction. If you don't have one in your RUCKSACK, you'll have to guess which instruction to follow.

If you think B2	go to 304
If you think C2	go to 5
If you think D2	go to 113

37

'Perhaps my suggestion wasn't such a good one after all!' said George when they had been walking for a good mile or so and still hadn't reached anywhere they recognised. Then she spotted two tiny figures sitting on the grass in the distance. 'Do you think it's that man and woman again?' she asked excitedly. 'If it is, then we must be nearly back where we started from!' They were just about to go nearer to get a better look when Julian suddenly remembered their binoculars. It would be much quicker if they had a look through them!

Use your BINOCULARS CARD to see if it's the man and woman or not by placing exactly over the shape below – then follow the instruction. If you don't have one, go to 151 instead.

'Timmy looks thirsty,' said George, when they had gone a short way further, 'let's stop so I can give him some of my ginger beer!' As soon as they had sat down, therefore, she poured some of her drink into a special cup she had brought for him. 'While I'm at it, I think perhaps I'll have some myself,' she added, taking a great big gulp from the bottle. The others all started laughing, suddenly realising *she* was the one who really wanted the drink!

Take one PICNIC CARD from your LUNCHBOX. Now go to 91.

There were several woods shown on their maps, however, and it was difficult to tell which one this was. 'We'll just have to wait until we reach some other landmark,' Julian sighed as he put his map away again. **Go to 53.**

Just as they were opening their codebooks, however, the dust got into Timmy's throat and he started coughing. 'Oh no,' cried Anne, as she glanced back at the floor, 'his coughing's blown the message away!' George quickly came to her dog's defence before anyone had a chance to tell him off. 'Timmy couldn't help it,' she said passionately. 'We would have spluttered as well if we'd got dust in our throats.' The others said they weren't going to tell him off, though. All they were going to suggest was that George gave Timmy some of her drink to help wash the dust down! 'Oh, I see,' she replied rather guiltily as she began to pour a little of her ginger beer into Timmy's special cup.

Take one PICNIC CARD from your LUNCHBOX. Now go to 10.

41

It was eventually Timmy who volunteered to climb the stairs first, as if deciding it was only right since he was the dog! They were just beginning to feel their way along the dark landing at the top when they suddenly heard someone singing. 'W-w-what's that?' asked George, thinking it might be the ghost of a former occupant. But then they noticed that the voice was coming from a portable radio on the floor. 'One of us must have kicked it on,' said Dick. They all fell silent as the singing was suddenly interrupted by a newsflash. It said that the escaped prisoner had finally been caught again near Sunken Lane. After they had switched the radio off, they decided to look up Sunken Lane on their maps to see how far away it was.

Use your MAP CARD to find which square Sunken Lane is in – then follow the instruction. If you don't have one, you'll have to guess which instruction to follow.

If you think A2	go to 105
If you think C2	go to 81
If you think B3	go to 283

They all suddenly went quiet as they heard footsteps above! 'Someone's coming into the house,' George exclaimed with horror. 'Oh, say they should come down here!' The footsteps stayed where they were, though, and a man started to talk. 'There must be two of them,' whispered Julian, '– let's creep back up the stairs and see if we can hear what's being said.' The speaker's voice was still fairly unclear but they could just make out something about the jewels being hidden in the lake, and that he would come back and dive for them after dark in case there was anybody about. Julian tried to get a better look at the two people by opening the cellar door a tiny bit more but they were too far away to see. 'Quick, someone hand me a pair of binoculars!' he whispered back to the others.

*Use your **BINOCULARS CARD** to try and see what the people looked like by placing exactly over the shape below – then follow the instruction. If you don't have one, go to 106.*

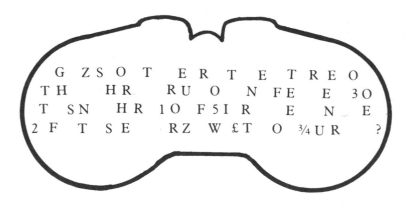

Just at that moment, though, one of the willows at the far end of the lake was suddenly caught by a strong wind. As its trailing branches were blown aside, a small wooden hut was revealed! 'We don't need to consult our maps after all,' Dick exclaimed. 'I bet that's a boathouse!' Running up to it, they found that he was right. And, although there were no boats inside, there *was* a small raft – which would do just as well! ***Go to 57.***

Timmy gave a couple of loud woofs, showing that *he* wanted to paddle the raft! The others wondered how he was going to hold the branch but he just ignored it. Instead, he plunged into the water at the back of the raft, starting to push it with his nose as he swam. That was *his* method of doing the paddling! He had pushed them quite a way into the lake when Julian noticed that someone had painted a message on one of the water-lilies. *PADDLE 50 METRES IN THE DIRECTION OF THE TREE WITH THE BLUE CROSS ON ITS TRUNK*, it read. Looking along the bank, they at last spotted this tree. All they needed now was their measuring tapes!

Use your MEASURE CARD to measure the 50 metres from the water-lily – then follow the instruction there. If you don't have one, you'll have to guess which instruction to follow.

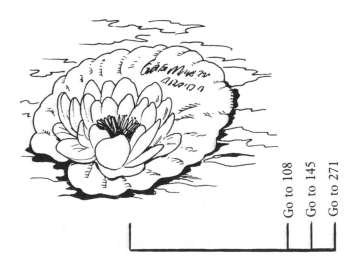

Go to 108

Go to 145

Go to 271

45

Julian put the jewels away again and carefully placed the bag at the bottom of his rucksack. 'We must get back to the village and show these to the police as quickly as possible,' he said, as they paddled back to the bank, '– then there might be time for them to trap those two villains when they come to dive for the jewels themselves after dark!' So, as soon as they had pulled the raft ashore, they started the long journey back across the countryside. 'I hope we're not going to be too late,' Anne panted after a couple of miles or so, noticing that the daylight was beginning to fade already! ***Go to 180.***

46

While George was looking for her binoculars, however, a voice just carried towards them through the quiet air and they realised there *was* someone there! Moments later, they could just make out two people – one quite a lot shorter than the other. They were obviously the same two people that had been in the mansion! George's throat was becoming so dry with tension that she had a quick drink of her ginger beer!

Take one PICNIC CARD from your LUNCHBOX. Now go to 247. (Remember: when there are no picnic cards left in your lunchbox, the game is over and you must start again.)

It looked as if they had no choice but to agree on Timmy's idea for he suddenly charged up to the village postman as he came out of someone's gate! 'Don't worry, he won't bite you,' the children laughed as they all ran after him, 'he just wants to ask you the way!' When they had told Timmy to calm down, they explained that they were looking for Sinister Lake. 'Sinister Lake?' repeated the postman, scratching his head. 'Well, let me see, you want to head for the little stone bridge and then follow the river downstream. That will point you in the right direction.' He said that the bridge was just before the parish church and so they all started looking for their maps in their rucksacks to find out how to get there.

Do you have a MAP in your RUCKSACK? If so, use it to find which square the parish church is in – then follow the instruction. (Remember to put the CARD back in your RUCKSACK afterwards.) If you don't have a MAP CARD in your RUCK-SACK, you'll have to guess which number to go to.

If you think D1	go to 17
If you think E1	go to 74
If you think E2	go to 160

George insisted on going first along the path herself, and, not wanting an argument, the others let her. They knew how moody she could sometimes become! It wasn't long, however, before the path ended at some fields and they wondered which way to go next. While they were trying to decide, Dick suddenly noticed a scrap of paper attached to one of the hooks of a barbed-wire fence. He carefully lifted it off, finding that it carried a message. *TO GET TO SINISTER LAKE* . . . it began, but the rest seemed to be in some sort of code. 'Quick, let's take out our codebooks!' he said excitedly, looking through his rucksack.

Use your CODEBOOK CARD to find out the rest of the direction by decoding the instruction below. If you don't have one in your RUCKSACK, go to 248 instead.

49

They soon found the footpath across the fields and they started to follow it. They now all had a little less picnic with them because, just before they left the fisherman, they offered him some of their sandwiches. He had found them so delicious that he had asked if he could have an extra one to crumble up as bait! 'He's probably catching them in the hundreds by now!' laughed Dick as they continued along.

Take one PICNIC CARD from your LUNCHBOX. Now go to 163.

50

Before they started off again, Dick asked if they could have a short rest. 'I feel as if my feet are about to drop off!' he said as he wearily plonked himself on to the ground. The others sat down, too, Julian deciding to have a drink of his ginger beer. But all the walking had made it so fizzy that a lot of it escaped down the side of the bottle and over the grass. 'Never mind,' laughed George as Timmy joyfully started to lap it up. 'At least someone got a drink even if you didn't!'

Take one PICNIC CARD from your LUNCHBOX. Now go to 90.

51

Before anyone could jump the brook, Dick attracted their attention. 'Come and look at this,' he called, crouching by a large flat stone, 'there's a message on it!' They all gathered round, George reading the message out. *'TO CROSS BROOK,'* she read, *'WALK 130 PACES FURTHER ALONG.'* As they started to count the paces, they discussed who could have written the message. 'It was probably some scouts in an orienteering game,' said Julian.

Use your MEASURE CARD to count these 130 paces – then follow the instruction there. If you don't have one, you'll have to guess which instruction to follow.

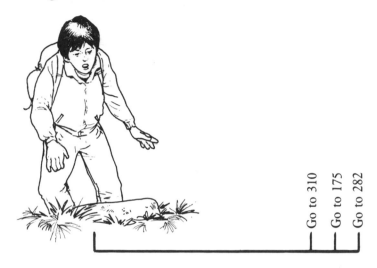

Go to 310
Go to 175
Go to 282

52

Before anyone had a chance to find the observation tower on their maps, however, Dick told them of a much better idea for seeing how much further the lake was. 'Why don't I just *climb* the tower?' he asked. 'The lake will probably be visible from the top!' The others were rather doubtful about it, though, noticing how old and rickety the tower looked. 'Don't worry, I'm sure it will be all right!' Dick told them and he took off his rucksack, ready to scale the long ladder. He had only climbed four rungs, however, when the ladder suddenly collapsed and he fell to the bottom. 'You're lucky you weren't hurt,' George told him, giving him some of her ginger beer to help him get over the shock!

Take one PICNIC CARD from your LUNCHBOX. Now go to 91.

The wood seemed to go on and on and they were wondering whether they were just walking round and round in circles. 'No, we can't be,' said George, 'or Timmy would have sniffed our scent from before.' So they decided just to keep following the twisting little path, hoping the lake would appear soon. They had only gone a few steps further when Julian tripped over a bramble. When he opened his lunchbox, he found that his bottle of ginger beer had broken and the box was swimming with liquid! 'It's a good job my cake and sandwiches were wrapped in foil,' he said, trying to look on the bright side, 'or that would have been the end of them as well!'

Take one PICNIC CARD from your LUNCHBOX. Now go to 176. (Remember: when there are no picnic cards left in your lunchbox, the game is over and you must start again.)

54

The mansion looked so spooky, however, that no one would volunteer to go in first! For once, even Timmy seemed a little nervous! 'Er – why don't we see if it's shown on our maps first?' suggested Dick, trying to put off the dreadful moment for as long as possible. 'It's probably better to do it out here because there won't be so much light inside!' So, grateful for this temporary excuse, they all began to search their rucksacks. It was the one time they weren't in too much of a hurry about it!

Use your MAP CARD to find which square the old mansion is in – then follow the instruction. If you don't have one, you'll have to guess which instruction to follow.

If you think B4	go to 92
If you think C4	go to 129
If you think A4	go to 196

55

They had counted just over half of the forty paces when Anne suddenly stepped on an old wine-bottle on the floor and slipped. 'I was lucky not to hurt myself,' she said as she dusted herself down, 'that could have been dangerous!' She stood up again but she was surprised to hear the bottle still rolling around by her feet. 'That's strange,' she said, 'I was sure I heard it break as I fell!' Suddenly, though, it dawned on her. If it wasn't the bottle on the floor that had broken it must have been the one in her lunchbox. So that was the end of her ginger beer.

Take one PICNIC CARD from your LUNCHBOX. Now go to 42.

56

They all suddenly jumped with fright as they heard a noise from the ground floor below. 'There's someone there!' Julian exclaimed as they could just make out the sound of a man talking. Keeping absolutely quiet, they tried to work out what he was saying. 'It's something to do with the jewels being hidden in a sunken rowing-boat,' Dick whispered to the others. 'He's telling the other person that they'll come back and dive for them after dark just in case there's anybody about.' Finally, the two people left and The Five started to discuss all this. 'If the jewels are in a sunken rowing-boat, then it must mean they're in the lake somewhere!' said Julian excitedly. Before they went to explore the lake, however, Dick insisted that they look at their maps to see where there was an island in a river. He had heard the man say that that's where his diving equipment was hidden and it might be useful information to give to the police.

Use your MAP CARD to find which square the river island is in – then follow the instruction. If you don't have one, you'll have to guess which instruction to follow.

If you think C3	go to 131
If you think D3	go to 12
If you think E2	go to 157

57

After searching round for a strong branch to use as a paddle, they navigated the raft into the middle of the lake. They then let it drift in the slight wind while they all peered over the side for anything at the bottom of the water. 'Look, there's a sunken rowing-boat!' shouted Dick, after a while, and they could just make out a large polythene bag tucked into its stern. Since it was far too deep to reach, Julian decided he would just have to dive for it – but before he could strip down to his shorts, Timmy had plunged in ahead of him! There was a long anxious wait but then Timmy finally surfaced again with the bag between his teeth. *Go to 119.*

58

Anne offered to do the paddling, squatting at the front of the raft so she could see where she was going. She had paddled quite a way out when she spotted a small plastic ball floating on the surface of the water. To begin with, she thought some child had lost it but then she realised that it was a buoy. 'Perhaps it's to mark the site of the jewels!' she said excitedly and paddled nearer. When it was only a metre or so away, she noticed that there was a message written on it. *PADDLE 50 METRES IN THE DIRECTION OF THE BOUNDARY STONE*, it read. They could just see a tall monument on a distant hill behind the trees and they assumed that it must be the boundary stone. All they needed now was their measuring tapes!

Use your MEASURE CARD to measure the 50 metres from the buoy – then follow the instruction there. If you don't have one, you'll have to guess which instruction to follow.

Go to 201

Go to 108

Go to 271

59

Quite a bit further on, they spotted a small road running between the fields some distance ahead. At the side of the road, there was a white signpost pointing to the left. 'I wonder if that points to the village?' asked George hopefully. 'What a shame we can't read it from here!' But then she suddenly remembered there *was* a way she could read it – with her binoculars! She quickly started looking for them in her rucksack.

*Use your **BINOCULARS CARD** to make the sign readable by placing exactly over the shape below – then follow the instruction. If you don't have one, go to 170 instead.*

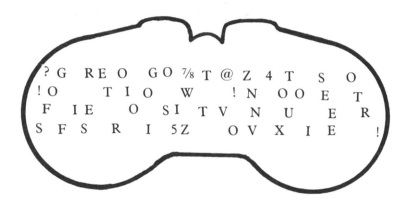

60

The others let Anne sit next to the pilot and she told him to fly south of the village. 'Ooh, isn't this fun!' she cried as they whirred across the countryside. She suddenly spotted a windmill, its white sails just visible in the darkness below, and she decided to look it up on her map to find out how much further they had to go.

*Use your **MAP CARD** to find which square the windmill is in – then follow the instruction. If you don't have one, you'll have to guess which instruction to follow.*

If you think C2	go to 86
If you think B3	go to 121
If you think C3	go to 265

In the end they agreed on George's idea – to go back to the village police station and ask them. 'Oh no, not you lot again!' the desk-sergeant sighed. 'What do you want this time?' George said that they had decided to unravel the mystery of the note themselves and asked if he knew how to get to Sinister Lake. 'Well, you're only wasting your time, if you want my opinion,' the sergeant replied, '– but, if you must go, then take the little turning a hundred paces further down the road. That will set you in the right direction.' As soon as they were back outside the police station, therefore, they started counting the hundred paces.

Use your MEASURE CARD to count the 100 paces from the police station yourself – then follow the instruction there. (Remember to put the CARD back in your RUCKSACK afterwards.) If you don't have one in your RUCKSACK, you'll have to guess which instruction to follow.

Go to 2

Go to 212

Go to 111

62

Just as they started to look for their binoculars, however, Dick thought of a more exciting way of finding out what the signpost said. 'Why don't we paddle across to the other bank?' he suggested, beginning to take off his socks and shoes. 'The river's really not that deep and I just feel like a nice cool dip!' So the others joined him in the water, slowly making their way to the other side. 'Oh no!' exclaimed Julian with a chuckle when the sign was at last clear enough to read, 'all it says is *NO PADDLING*!' **Go to 233.**

63

The scribbled code worked out as a man's name – *REG STONE*. 'I wouldn't mind betting that's the escaped prisoner's name,' Julian remarked as they put their codebooks back in their rucksacks. He added that he had probably signed the note in code in case it fell into the wrong hands. Dick carefully folded the piece of paper up again before they continued on their way. **Go to 163.**

64

Some distance further, they had to come to a sudden stop because a brook flowed right across where they wanted to go. Unfortunately, it was just a bit too wide to jump. 'Let's see if we can find a narrower part,' said Julian, leading the way along the bank. It didn't become much narrower but they finally reached a section that looked just about possible. 'Right, who's going to jump first?' asked Julian.

Throw the FAMOUS FIVE DICE to decide.

JULIAN thrown	go to 295
DICK thrown	go to 252
GEORGE thrown	go to 21
ANNE thrown	go to 139
TIMMY thrown	go to 102
MYSTERY thrown	go to 51

65

Anne had led them about half way along the stepping-stones when she noticed an old signpost thirty metres or so to their right. Unfortunately, though, it was just too far away to read and they couldn't go any nearer because it was right in the middle of the marsh! 'I expect it was put there when the marsh was still dry land,' said Julian. They were just about to start walking again when George suddenly thought of a way they *could* read it, after all. 'We can look at it through our binoculars!' she said.

Use your BINOCULARS CARD to read what the signpost said by placing exactly over the shape below – then follow the instruction. If you don't have one, go to 174 instead.

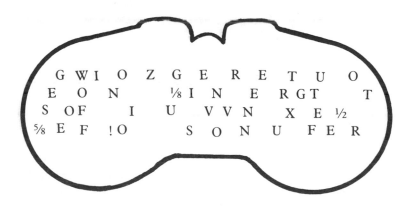

```
  G  WI  O  Z  G  E    R    E   T   U     O
 E  O   N    ⅛ I  N  E  R GT        T
 S  OF    I   U   V V N    X  E  ½
⅝ E  F  ! O        S   O   N    U   F E R
```

66

They were just about to open their codebooks, however, when Dick noticed that another of the trees had a sign nailed to it. 'Hey, look – it points to Sinister Lake!' he told the others excitedly. So they decided just to leave the coded message and continue on their way. 'It must be just on the other side of the wood!' said Anne as they hurried along the twisting path. But, unfortunately, they were in a bit too much of a hurry because Dick suddenly tripped over George's feet and crashed to the ground. When he looked in his lunchbox, he found that not only had his bottle of ginger beer broken but it had ruined all his sandwiches and cake as well!

Take one PICNIC CARD from your LUNCHBOX. Now go to 176. (Remember: when there are no picnic cards left in your lunchbox, the game is over and you must start again.)

67

Fortunately, the code used in the message *was* the same as the one in their codebooks! It said that they were to look behind the blue lady. 'I wonder what that means,' said Dick but then he suddenly noticed an old portrait on the wall. It was of somebody who looked like a countess, in a blue dress! They all rushed over to it, discovering that it concealed a secret hole. 'Look, there's a small measuring tape inside,' exclaimed Julian, putting in his hand. 'It must have been used by that prisoner when he originally came to hide the jewels, so he would know where to find them again!'

If you don't already have it, put the MEASURE CARD into your RUCKSACK. Now go to 10.

68

Anne eventually volunteered to climb the stairs first, but only on condition that the others stayed right behind her! Finally reaching the landing at the top, they noticed a small window at the far end and they decided to edge towards that so they could see better. Peering through the broken glass, they could just make out the top of a windmill sail in the far distance. Dick then suggested looking up the windmill on their maps so they would know which direction they were facing.

Use your MAP CARD to find which square the windmill is in – then follow the instruction. If you don't have one, you'll have to guess which instruction to follow.

If you think B2	go to 81
If you think C2	go to 177
If you think D2	go to 283

'Oh, I've never known such scare-babies,' George remarked, suddenly becoming impatient, and she decided just to lead the way down the cellar steps herself! It was very dark at the bottom and they all stuck close to the cellar wall, running their hands along the cold stone. Suddenly, George felt a series of grooves in the wall, as if someone had chiselled out a message! 'Yes, it is a message,' she exclaimed as she started to trace each letter with her finger, 'it says . . . *WALK – FORTY – PACES – FURTHER – ALONG.*' The others felt the message too, just to make sure she had got it right, and then they all began to count the forty paces!

Use your MEASURE CARD to count the 40 paces yourself – then follow the instruction there. If you don't have one, you'll have to guess which instruction to follow.

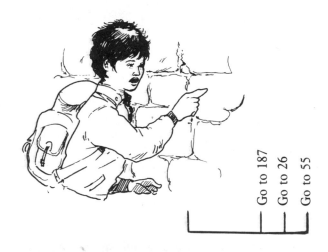

Go to 187

Go to 26

Go to 55

Reaching the eighty-metre mark on their tapes, they found they had come to a thick pile of branches. 'I wonder what's so special about these?' asked Dick, bewilderedly, but then it occurred to him that they might be hiding something. Quickly pulling the branches off, he found that he was right – for there was a small raft underneath! As they lifted it up to carry it back to the lake, George noticed that there was something else there. 'It's a map,' she exclaimed. 'Let's take it with us as a spare!'

If you don't already have it, put the MAP CARD into your RUCKSACK. Now go to 95.

71

George kept insisting they should follow *her* suggestion and, since there wasn't really time to argue, they agreed. She led them towards a small river in the distance, sure that that was the one that ran through the outskirts of the village. So when they finally reached it, they started to follow it through the fields. After about half an hour or so, they came to a small waterfall and Julian suggested they look it up on their maps just to make certain that this *was* the river that flowed near the village.

Use your MAP CARD to find which square the small waterfall is in (look carefully!) – then follow the instruction. If you don't have one, you'll have to guess which instruction to follow.

If you think C2	go to 319
If you think D3	go to 158
If you think D2	go to 94

Julian was right – the coded message *did* say that the jewels were hidden on the boat! So they all had a closer look at the inside of the boat, putting their heads just below the surface of the water this time. Dick could just make out a large polythene bag tucked into the stern of the boat. 'The jewels must be in there,' he said excitedly as he came up for air! *Go to 240.*

No sooner had they reached the raft than they heard two lots of footsteps coming towards the lake and someone talking. The sergeant immediately ordered them all to hide behind a nearby group of trees. As they were crouching down, Dick suddenly noticed something lying amongst the grass. 'Look, it's a codebook!' he whispered to the sergeant and the sergeant told him to pop it into his rucksack in case it belonged to the escaped prisoner. It might be useful evidence against him!

If you don't already have it, put the CODEBOOK CARD into your RUCKSACK. Now go to 247.

'It looks as if we have to turn left at the next junction,' said Julian, after they had found the parish church on their maps. They had still to reach the bridge when Anne suddenly spotted a leather disc in the grass verge. Picking it up, she discovered that it was an old type of measuring tape. 'It must have been left by the men from the council when they were surveying the road,' remarked Julian. Since it was probably quite important, they decided to take it with them so they could hand it in at the town hall the next time they were there.

If you don't already have it, put the MEASURE CARD into your RUCKSACK. Now go to 136.

Following Julian along the narrow footpath, they soon reached a field and they could all walk side by side once more. George said it was about time they asked the direction again and so they looked to see if anyone was about. 'Yes, there's someone!' exclaimed Anne, pointing to a solitary figure right in the centre of the field. When they reached the figure, however, they all burst into laughter – for it was just an old scarecrow! 'I know,' said Dick as they were wondering what to do now, 'let's see if we can spot the lake through our binoculars!' So they all started searching through their rucksacks for them.

Use your BINOCULARS CARD to try and spot the lake yourself by placing exactly over the shape below – then follow the instruction. If you don't have one in your RUCKSACK, go to 296 instead.

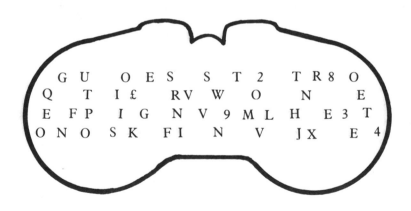

The coded message finally worked out as: *MEET AT MRS TAGGART'S BARN JUST AFTER MIDNIGHT.* 'So we were right,' Julian exclaimed as they put their codebooks away again, 'it *was* the escaped prisoner that called on Dick!' They had only gone a few steps further from the bundle of clothes when Anne spotted a leather case lying amongst the reeds. 'Look, it's a pair of binoculars,' she said as she opened it up. 'This must have belonged to the escaped prisoner as well, and he left it on the ground when he changed his clothes!'

If you don't already have it, put the BINOCULARS CARD into your RUCKSACK. Now go to 233.

77

They were just about to start counting the 170 paces when the man said he would show them the sheep-track himself, since it was quite easy to miss. So as soon as he had dried the last of his pans, he led the way along the bank. 'There it is,' he said finally, pointing to a faint path in the grass, '— just keep following it to the end!' To show how grateful they were for his help, George gave the man a piece of her cake. 'It's delicious,' she told him, 'and it will make a nice change from all that stew you're probably eating!'

Take one PICNIC CARD from your LUNCHBOX. Now go to 24.

'I'll go first myself,' said Dick and he led the way to the other end. They hadn't walked much further from the stepping-stones when they noticed a hut standing on tall wooden stilts a short distance ahead. 'It's probably for observing birds,' said Julian as they came closer and he began to wonder whether the tower might be shown on their maps. If it was, it would be a clue as to how much further they had to go. So they all slipped off their rucksacks to take their maps out.

Use your MAP CARD to find which square the observation tower is in – then follow the instruction. If you don't have one, you'll have to guess which instruction to follow.

If you think D2	go to 52
If you think D3	go to 268
If you think C3	go to 91

They soon came to a large wood and, rather than walking all the way round, they decided it would be much quicker to go straight through the middle. But it wasn't long before they were regretting the decision because they seemed to be getting more and more lost. 'I'm sure we've already come this way once!' said George as the path twisted and turned. They hadn't gone much further when Anne suddenly noticed that one of the trees had a message carved into its bark. 'It looks like it's in some sort of code,' said Julian excitedly as they all gathered round to examine it. They were soon slipping off their rucksacks to look for their codebooks!

Use your CODEBOOK CARD to find out what the message said by decoding the instruction below. If you don't have one, go to 66 instead.

80

The coded message said that the bag contained an assortment of safe-breaking tools. 'Of course, that's what they are,' exclaimed Julian. 'They must belong to that prisoner!' He said that he had probably brought them there just after his burglary but had forgotten them when he went to find a hiding-place for the jewels. Later, of course, he was put in prison and so he couldn't come back and collect them! *Go to 10.*

As they put their maps away again, Anne could hear a slight hissing sound coming from nearby. She eventually traced it to her lunchbox and opened the lid. 'Oh no,' she cried, 'my bottle of ginger beer must have become fizzed up as we were climbing the stairs. I didn't do the cap up properly either – so a lot of it has leaked out!' Fortunately, though, it hadn't yet soaked into her cake or sandwiches and therefore wasn't a total disaster!

Take one PICNIC CARD from your LUNCHBOX. Now go to 117.

82

At last finding the sundial in the house's grounds, they suddenly realised there was a problem. They knew they had to measure sixty metres from it but they didn't know which way! Since it could take ages trying out every direction, they decided not to bother. 'Oh well,' said George, 'at least we now know the jewels are hidden in the lake – and that's much more important!' They were in such a hurry to make their way back to the lake, however, that Julian tripped over a piece of broken statue in the long grass. He was so pleased that he hadn't hurt himself that he didn't notice his codebook had slipped out of his rucksack!

If you have it, remove the CODEBOOK CARD from your RUCKSACK. Now go to 157.

Anne hadn't led them far round the edge of the lake when she suddenly had an idea! 'Why don't we look up the lake on our maps and see if it shows a boathouse anywhere?' she suggested. 'You never know, there might be one hidden behind those large trees at the far end!' So as soon as they had found their maps, they quickly started looking for the section with the lake.

Use your MAP CARD to find out which square the lake is in – then follow the instruction. If you don't have one, you'll have to guess which instruction to follow.

If you think D4	go to 315
If you think B4	go to 43
If you think C4	go to 144

George was just taking her binoculars out, however, when the small brown object suddenly flew up into the air! 'So much for your marker, George,' the others all fell about laughing, '– it's just a duck!' The duck circled the lake a couple of times and then came skidding towards their raft. 'It must be after something to eat,' said Anne, and she took out one of her sandwiches, tearing off little pieces for it.

Take one PICNIC CARD from your LUNCHBOX. Now go to 120.

85

Anne was in such a hurry to find her codebook that her map fell out of her rucksack as she was rummaging through it. In trying to catch it, she merely knocked it over the raft's edge and into the water! It quickly sank before she could reach it, draping itself right over the coded message on the wrecked boat. So she had not only lost her map but they could no longer work the message out!

If you have it, remove the MAP CARD from your RUCKSACK. Now go to 240.

86

It was only a few minutes more before they could see something shimmering in the moonlight below and they realised it must be the lake! So the pilot started to take the helicopter down, landing it as near to the lake as possible. 'Good, they're not here yet!' said the sergeant when they had walked through the wood and finally stood at the water's edge. He then suggested that they all hide behind a group of trees just back from the lake, waiting for the two people to appear. Nearly half an hour had passed when George thought she saw someone approach amongst the trees some distance to her right. She quickly searched for her binoculars to get a better look!

*Use your **BINOCULARS CARD** to see whether there was someone there or not by placing exactly over the shape below – then follow the instruction. If you don't have one, go to 46 instead.*

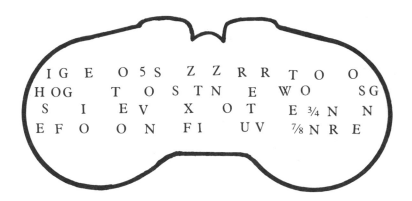

They were still trying to decide whose idea to follow when George suddenly noticed they were standing outside the village library and on the wall was a large map of the village. They all gathered round to have a closer look. Although it didn't show Sinister Lake itself, it had an arrow pointing in its direction at the very edge of the map. The arrow was right next to a little bridge across a river and so Julian suggested that they made their way to that. 'We should have come to it by now, surely,' said Dick when they had been walking for a good quarter of an hour or so. Just to check they were going the right way, therefore, Anne suggested seeing if they could spot the bridge with their binoculars.

*Use your **BINOCULARS CARD** to see if the bridge is ahead or not by placing exactly over the shape below – then follow the* instruction. *(Remember to put the CARD back in your RUCK-SACK afterwards.) If you don't have one in your RUCKSACK, go to 148 instead.*

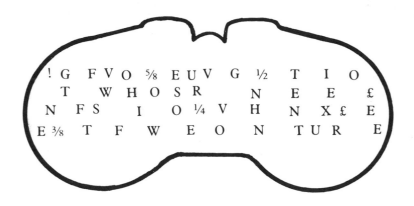

88

'It's about another quarter of a mile,' said Dick, when he was the first to find the stile on his map. On the way, Anne asked why they built stiles and didn't just have a hole in the fence. Julian replied that it was to allow people to pass through, but not sheep and other farm animals. 'Anyway, they're a lot more fun than a hole would be!' he added with a chuckle. *Go to 224.*

89

'This must be it!' said George, finding the start of a narrow track right next to the sixty-metre mark. So as soon as they had put their measuring tapes away again, they began to follow it across the fields. After what the fisherman had been saying, though, they secretly wondered whether they really wanted to go to Sinister Lake after all! It was a good job they all kept their thoughts to themselves or they might well have changed each other's minds! *Go to 163.*

The Five had walked quite a bit further when they suddenly came across a large area of marshland. They were wondering how they were going to get to the other side but then Dick noticed a series of stepping-stones twisting right through the middle. 'They were probably put there by local farmers,' said Julian as they hurried up to where the stones started. Some of the stones were very narrow, though, and Dick recommended that they should go one at a time so they didn't knock each other off!

Throw the FAMOUS FIVE DICE to decide who is to go first.

JULIAN thrown	go to 259
DICK thrown	go to 78
GEORGE thrown	go to 216
ANNE thrown	go to 65
TIMMY thrown	go to 184
MYSTERY thrown	go to 152

Not long after, they spotted a couple of long, slender birds flying up from a circle of trees in the distance. 'They look like herons,' said Julian – and then he remembered that herons always lived near water! 'Perhaps it means the lake's amongst those trees!' he told them, suddenly becoming all excited. They were just about to start running in that direction when George made them wait for a second. 'So that we don't go all that way for nothing,' she suggested, 'let's just make sure they *are* herons first by looking through our binoculars.' The others thought it a good idea, quickly opening their rucksacks!

Use your BINOCULARS CARD to get a better look at the birds by placing exactly over the shape below – then follow the instruction. If you don't have one, go to 8 instead.

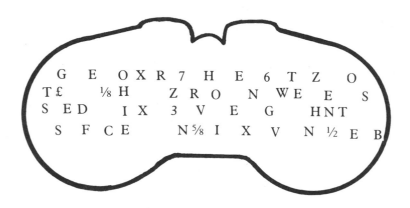

```
G   E   O X R 7  H   E  6 T Z    O
T£       ⅛ H      Z R O  N  WE   E      S
S  ED      I X  3  V     E   G      H N T
   S   F  C E       N ⅝ I   X   V   N ½  E  B
```

92

'Are you *sure* that's this one?' George asked when the boys had found a mansion on their maps. She knew it was really but she was just trying to put off having to go inside for a little longer! 'Yes, it must be,' replied Dick, showing her the map again. 'Look, there's a lake right next to it!' Unable to delay it any more, therefore, they now returned to the question of who was going to enter the mansion first. 'Oh, I'm sure it can't be that bad!' said Julian and he quickly pushed the door open before he had time to think about it. 'Gosh, I've never seen so much dust,' remarked Anne as she and the others cautiously followed him across the dark floor. 'It looks as if there hasn't been anyone here for ages!' ***Go to 10.***

'Oh, this is hopeless,' sighed Julian as they were still trying to find their binoculars in their rucksacks. 'I don't know whether I keep touching them or not. It's so difficult to tell!' In fact, he was becoming so irritated by it that he decided just to lead the way up the stairs without worrying what was up there! 'It *seems* alright,' he whispered to the others as they followed him on to the shadowy landing. Anne's throat became so dry with tension, however, that she had to have a quick drink of her ginger beer!

Take one PICNIC CARD from your LUNCHBOX. Now go to 117.

Finding a waterfall on her map, Anne then followed the river along with her finger to see where it went. 'Yes, it *does* run just outside the village!' she exclaimed. So they continued to walk along its bank – but soon breaking into a trot because they noticed the daylight was beginning to fade already! Dick suddenly stopped, however, to pick something up from the ground. It was a measuring tape, and he decided to take it with him to hand in to the police.

If you don't already have it, put the MEASURE CARD into your RUCKSACK. Now go to 59.

They were just about to push the raft out into the water when they realised they had nothing to paddle it with. 'I know – we'll use that branch over there!' said Dick, noticing one that was nice and straight and with quite a thick end. They now all squeezed on to the raft, using the branch to ease it away from the mud. 'Right, who's going to do the paddling?' asked George as soon as they were afloat.

Throw the FAMOUS FIVE DICE to decide.

JULIAN thrown	go to 284
DICK thrown	go to 246
GEORGE thrown	go to 15
ANNE thrown	go to 58
TIMMY thrown	go to 44
MYSTERY thrown	go to 189

96

'Yes, it *is* the right one,' exclaimed Anne as she studied her map. 'Look, after about another two miles or so the river passes very close to the village church!' They felt a lot happier now they were positive they were on the right track but Julian was becoming a little worried about the time. The daylight was beginning to fade already! ***Go to 59.***

97

'Right, this should be far enough now!' said Julian, and the others tried to keep the raft steady while he put his face right down to the water. 'Can you see anything?' Anne asked excitedly but he shook his head, crawling across to the other side of the raft. Suddenly, he gave a shout! 'Yes,' I *can* see something,' he exclaimed. 'It's a sunken rowing-boat and there's some sort of coded message along the side. I wouldn't mind betting it says that the jewels are hidden inside the boat!' So they quickly looked for their codebooks to see if Julian was right!

Use your CODEBOOK CARD to find out what the message said by decoding the instruction below. If you don't have one, go to 85 instead.

98

'The prison is about a mile too far east of the lake,' Anne told the pilot as soon as she had found it on her map, 'so you need to go back a bit!' As the helicopter made its sharp turn, something started sliding along the floor, stopping at the sergeant's feet. 'Why, it's a measuring tape,' he exclaimed, bending down. 'It must have fallen out of that prisoner's pocket when we picked him up!'

If you don't already have it, put the MEASURE CARD into your RUCKSACK. Now go to 110.

99

As they were looking for their codebooks, however, there was a sudden gust of wind and it blew the scrap of paper into the river! Timmy was about to jump in after it but George held on to him, knowing that it would no longer be readable by now. 'What a nuisance,' said Julian disappointedly as they continued on their way, 'that message might have been something important!' **Go to 233.**

100

Just as they were about to start working out the scribbled code, they found that it had gone! Their fingers must have been so sticky with excitement that they had rubbed it off. Rather annoyed with themselves, they continued on their way. **Go to 163.**

101

Just as they were opening their maps, Julian noticed something gleaming at the end of the next valley. 'Look, it must be the lake,' he exclaimed, '– we needn't look up where we are after all!' So they eagerly set off in the valley's direction but they hadn't got very far when Dick tripped on a small rock in the grass. 'Oh, your poor knee!' Anne said – but all Dick cared about was checking his rucksack. As he fell, he thought he heard something crack inside! 'Oh no,' he cried as he opened the flap, 'I've broken my binoculars!'

If you have it, remove the BINOCULARS CARD from your RUCKSACK. Now go to 90.

102

Timmy insisted on jumping the brook first, making an excited leap to the other bank! The others took much longer about it, though, and he became so fed up waiting for them that he started to wander off on his own. By the time the children *were* all finally across, he had completely disappeared into the distance! 'Where is he?' asked

George anxiously but, as hard as they searched, they couldn't spot him. 'Perhaps we'll have more luck with our binoculars!' said Julian suddenly, and he immediately began to dig around for them in his rucksack.

*Use your **BINOCULARS CARD** to try and find Timmy by placing exactly over the shape below – then follow the instruction. If you don't have one, go to 195 instead.*

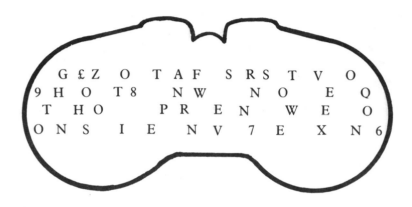

103

They had only gone a short way further when it suddenly started to rain. 'It's just a summer shower,' Julian said, glancing up at the sky, 'it should be over soon.' But it was still quite heavy and so they all hurriedly looked through their rucksacks for their waterproofs. 'Oh no, it's stopped now!' laughed Dick, just as he had put his on. When he returned it to his rucksack, he suddenly noticed that his codebook was missing. Thinking that it had probably fallen out some time ago, he just accepted that it was lost and said there was no point in going looking for it. In actual fact, he had accidentally pulled it out with his waterproof and it lay only some twenty metres behind them!

*If you have it, remove the **CODEBOOK CARD** from your **RUCKSACK**. Now go to 91.*

104

Continuing to explore the ground floor, they eventually entered what must have been the kitchen. There was a huge fireplace in the corner and they kept tripping over broken pots and pans. Timmy started sniffing at a large door and, opening it, the children discovered a flight of stone steps behind. 'They must lead down to the cellar,' said Dick and they decided they had better go and give that a search as well. They all waited for someone to offer to walk down first!

Throw the FAMOUS FIVE DICE to see who it's to be.

JULIAN thrown	go to 142
DICK thrown	go to 198
GEORGE thrown	go to 69
ANNE thrown	go to 288
TIMMY thrown	go to 262
MYSTERY thrown	go to 303

105

'Sunken Lane's about three miles away,' said Anne, holding her map right up to her face so she could see it. As they put their maps away again, Dick said that he felt a lot safer now that he knew the prisoner had been caught. According to the newsflash, he had seemed quite violent! ***Go to 117.***

106

By the time someone had found a pair of binoculars for Julian, though, the two people had left. 'Oh well, never mind,' he said, 'at least we now know the jewels are hidden in the lake!' Before they made their way back to the lake, however, they decided they had better stay in the cellar a while longer to make sure the people had well and truly gone. For something to do, they had a quick dip into their picnic!

Take one PICNIC CARD from your LUNCHBOX. Now go to 157. (Remember: when there are no picnic cards left in your lunchbox, the game is over and you must start again.)

107

Julian hadn't led them far round the edge of the lake when their path was blocked by a fallen tree. As they were clambering over, George noticed that someone had carved a message into the bark. When they pulled back some of the branches to get a better look, however, they realised that it was in code. 'Quick, let's take out our codebooks,' urged Anne, thinking it might say where a boat was hidden!

*Use your **CODEBOOK CARD** to find out what the message said by decoding the instruction below. If you don't have one, go to 289 instead.*

108
Dick was in such a hurry to get to his measuring tape, however, that the raft started to rock as he stretched across for his rucksack. 'Don't get too excited,' Anne cried with alarm, 'or you'll have us all in the water!' So he calmed himself down a bit, reaching for his rucksack a little more cautiously. *Go to 271.*

109
'Here it is,' said Anne as she pointed to the railway station on her map, '– at the west end of the village!' Unfortunately, the police station was at the other end and so it would probably mean at least another quarter of an hour walking between the two. 'We'd better go a bit faster!' said Julian when he realised. *Go to 180.*

Landing three or four hundred metres from the lake, the pilot then switched off his engine so they could all get out. 'Make sure you tread as quietly as possible,' the sergeant whispered back as he led the way through the trees, 'just in case those people are already there.' They finally reached the lake – it looking even more sinister in the dark! 'Good, they're not here yet,' said the sergeant, glancing round. 'So I suggest we hide fairly near to the raft, ready to trap them when they push it into the water. You remember where you left it, I hope?' Julian told him it was exactly 110 paces from an old PRIVATE PROPERTY sign, and so as soon as they had found the sign they started to count the paces.

Use your MEASURE CARD to count out the 110 paces yourself – then follow the instruction there. If you don't have one, you'll have to guess which instruction to follow.

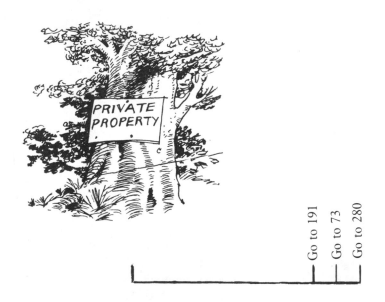

Go to 191
Go to 73
Go to 280

It wasn't long before the village was just a few small dots behind them and they were surrounded by the peaceful sounds of the countryside. Larks sang above and bees hummed around the clover. 'Ooh, isn't it a glorious day!' exclaimed Anne as they walked along. The lane they were in became smaller and smaller and it was soon little more than a narrow footpath. 'We'd better walk in single file,' said George, 'or we're going to be pushing each other into the hedges!'

Throw the FAMOUS FIVE DICE to decide who is to go first along the path.

JULIAN thrown	go to 75
DICK thrown	go to 161
GEORGE thrown	go to 48
ANNE thrown	go to 149
TIMMY thrown	go to 193
MYSTERY thrown	go to 18

'It says that the tobacco tin contains the plans for the escape!' Julian exclaimed when they had at last decoded the writing on the back. They wondered what escape it was talking about, but of course . . . it was the escape from the prison. The tin must have been given to the prisoner who was going to break out by a friend from outside during visiting time. And he had scratched the coded message on the back to let him know that there was more than just tobacco in it! 'Once the prisoner had reached here,' Julian remarked as they continued their journey, 'I suppose the plans had served their purpose and so he just threw them away!' ***Go to 233.***

113

They soon came to a small pond and, since it was so hot, George suggested stopping for a while so that Timmy could have a quick dip. While they watched him paddling about, Anne opened her lunchbox to check that the butter wasn't melting in her sandwiches. As she was about to put the lid back on, however, Timmy leapt out of the pond, spraying the sandwiches with water! 'Oh, look what you've done, Timmy!' she scolded him. 'Now I'll have to throw most of them out for the birds!'

Take one PICNIC CARD from your LUNCHBOX. Now go to 163.

114

Although Timmy couldn't tell them his suggestion, of course, he obviously had one, because he eagerly started tugging at George's sleeve. 'Okay, Timmy, we'll follow your route,' she said, since they didn't seem to have any choice! They thought that perhaps he had picked up their scent from when they had come – but they were soon to find that there was a totally different reason for his keenness. 'Oh no,' exclaimed Anne, 'he just wanted to bring us to all these rabbits!' There were hundreds and hundreds of them, all living on the same hill. They were just about to give Timmy a good telling-off when Dick suddenly remembered something. There was a hill in this area called Rabbit Hill and this was obviously it! 'So if we look up Rabbit Hill on our maps,' he continued, 'we should know roughly where we are!'

Use your MAP CARD to find which square Rabbit Hill is in – then follow the instruction. If you don't have one, you'll have to guess which instruction to follow.

If you think B3	go to 215
If you think D3	go to 183
If you think C3	go to 64

115

Dick was taking off his rucksack to look for his codebook when his arm became caught in one of the straps. In trying to wriggle free, he nearly slipped off the narrow stone into the marsh! Although he was just able to stop himself falling in, though, he could do nothing about his lunchbox. It had dropped from his hand in the shock and was now being sucked down into the mud!

Take one PICNIC CARD from your LUNCHBOX. Now go to 91.

116

Before they could find their maps, however, George suddenly asked them to listen. 'I've just been thinking,' she said in a worried voice, '– that person who rang was obviously expecting someone else to be here. That means they might well be arriving any minute!' So she suggested they get on with exploring the cellar as quickly as possible, leading the way down the steps. But they were in such a hurry that Anne tripped over Julian's feet, dropping her lunchbox. She could hear her bottle of ginger beer break inside as it tumbled all the way to the bottom!

Take one PICNIC CARD from your LUNCHBOX. Now go to 269.

117

They all suddenly froze on the spot as they heard the front door creak open downstairs! 'Quick, crouch down,' Julian ordered, 'there are two people coming in!' Although they couldn't quite see what the people looked like, they could just hear one of them talking. 'We'll come back and dive for the jewels after dark,' a man said in a low voice, '– just in case there's anybody about! I'll meet you back here at ten.' The two people then left and, having made absolutely sure they weren't going to come back again, The Five crept down to where they had been standing. 'Look, one of them dropped this!' exclaimed George, picking up a notebook. Opening it, they saw that there was a coded message inside and so they hurriedly looked for their codebooks.

Use your CODEBOOK CARD to find out what the message said by decoding the instruction below. If you don't have one, go to 27 instead.

118

'Look, he's over there by that railway line!' George cried joyfully as she suddenly saw Timmy through her binoculars. As they hurried towards him, they wondered why he should have been attracted by a railway but then Dick suddenly realised. 'Don't you see?' he asked eagerly, giving Timmy a pat for his cleverness. 'This must be the railway that runs into the village and so all we have to do is follow it!' *Go to 276.*

119

Giving Timmy a pat on the head, they emptied the bag on to the raft. 'Gosh, look at those,' exclaimed George as half-a-dozen glittering diamond necklaces poured out, 'they must be worth a fortune!' Julian put the jewels away again and carefully placed the bag at the bottom of his rucksack before they paddled back to the bank. 'We must get back to the village and show these to the police as quickly as possible,' he said as they pulled the raft ashore, '– then there might just be time for them to trap those two accomplices when they come searching for the jewels themselves after dark!' Unfortunately, though, they couldn't agree which direction to go for the village, each having a different suggestion!

Throw the FAMOUS FIVE DICE to decide whose suggestion they should follow.

JULIAN thrown	go to 229
DICK thrown	go to 255
GEORGE thrown	go to 71
ANNE thrown	go to 210
TIMMY thrown	go to 133
MYSTERY thrown	go to 29

120

Finally reaching the middle of the lake, they spotted a bright yellow fishing-float bobbing up and down in the water. They thought it must have come off someone's line and just drifted away but then they noticed that something seemed to be tying it down underneath. Paddling right up to it, they discovered that there was a tiny message scratched round the side! *TO FIND JEWELS*, they could just about read, *PADDLE 60 METRES TOWARDS THE TALLEST TREE ON THE BANK*. As soon as they had worked out which was the tallest tree, they eagerly started searching for a measuring tape!

Use your MEASURE CARD to measure the 60 metres from the float – then follow the instruction there. If you don't have one, you'll have to guess which instruction to follow.

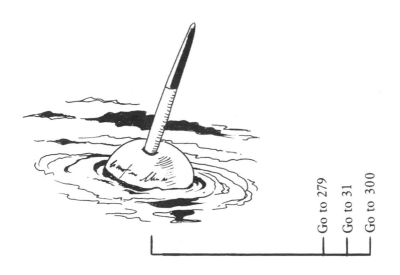

Go to 279   Go to 31   Go to 300

121

'I hope we're not going to be too late!' said the sergeant as the helicopter continued to hum through the dark sky. 'I know we've already recaptured the one who originally did the robbery but it would be nice to arrest his accomplices as well. Otherwise, they might well try and help him make another escape!' ***Go to 86.***

'It's about another half mile,' said George, who was the first to find the bridge on her map. As they continued towards it, they wondered what these bad stories were about the lake. 'Perhaps it's haunted by someone who was drowned there,' suggested Dick. Discussing it was giving them such goose-pimples, however, that they soon decided to change the subject! *Go to 136.*

As it turned out, they didn't need to count the paces for the turning was marked with a little green signpost! *TO SINISTER LAKE – 4¹/₂ MILES* it read. 'Fancy not noticing it the first time we passed,' Dick exclaimed. 'It shows how observant we all are!' Before they started in the direction the sign pointed, George suggested that they sit down for a quick rest and some of their picnic. 'After all, four and a half miles is still quite a long way,' she said, tucking into a sandwich.

Take one PICNIC CARD from your LUNCHBOX. Now go to 224.

George had only led them a short way along the river when she spotted a signpost on the other bank. They wondered whether it might point to the lake but it was just a bit too small to read from their side. 'We'll just have to hope we come across a signpost on *our* bank,' said Dick disappointedly, but then Anne suddenly had an idea. *Of course, it was so simple* – they could look at the sign through their binoculars!

Use your BINOCULARS CARD to find out where the sign

pointed by placing exactly over the shape below – then follow theinstruction. Ifyoudon'thaveoneinyourRUCKSACK,goto 62 instead.

```
    G  ST  O   N     HOE  E      T  R    O
 T    O  H   N   R 5    9     E £  E    U !
 S   EV O       R  EE  I X       I  G N    X
 F   T  H F     R   W   E   O  NEU      R
```

125
Anne's suggestion was to head for a ruined castle she had spotted a short distance to their left. 'A castle is bound to be shown on the map,' she explained to the others as they went, 'and so it should tell us roughly where we are.' As soon as they reached the castle, therefore, they hurriedly took their maps out.

Use your MAP CARD to find which square the ruined castle is in – then follow the instruction. If you don't have one, you'll have to guess which instruction to follow.

If you think C3	go to 50
If you think B3	go to 101
If you think A3	go to 20

126
While they were looking for their codebooks, however, a tame sparrow came along and picked the scrap of paper up in its beak! 'How are we going to get it back?' Dick whispered anxiously,

careful not to make it fly off. But then Anne suddenly had a clever idea. 'I know,' she said, 'I can offer it some of my cake. As soon as it goes to eat, it will have to drop the paper!' So she carefully crumbled a slice of her cake on to the ground but at that moment George suddenly gave a large sneeze, scaring the bird away. Not only did they no longer have the message but Anne had also wasted some of her food!

Take one PICNIC CARD from your LUNCHBOX. Now go to 24.

124

127

'He's over that way!' George cried, as she suddenly spotted Timmy through her binoculars. So they all ran after him, finally catching him up. 'You must wait for us in future!' they told him crossly, but their annoyance soon disappeared when they saw what he had in his mouth. 'Look, he's found a measuring tape!' said Julian, taking it from him to see if it still worked. It worked perfectly and it was also a lot longer than any of theirs and so they decided to take it with them. 'Perhaps he's not such a bad dog after all!' they all remarked with a laugh as they continued on their way.

If you don't already have it, put the MEASURE CARD into your RUCKSACK. Now go to 79.

128

George was in such a hurry to find her measuring tape that she accidentally gave the mirror a bit of a nudge. The next thing she knew it had crashed to the floor, shattering into thousands of pieces! 'Oh, you idiot,' exclaimed Dick. 'I can't remember how many metres it told us to measure!' Nor could the others and so they just had to forget about following the message. There was worse news! The crash had given Anne such a shock that she dropped her lunchbox. The lid had come open in the fall and many of her sandwiches were now much too dirty to eat!

Take one PICNIC CARD from your LUNCHBOX. Now go to 104.

129

They at last found the courage to enter the old mansion, all squeezing through the door more or less together. Most of the inside was very dark but there were shafts of light every so often from the broken windows. 'Gosh, it looks as if it hasn't been lived in for ages!' whispered Dick, noticing how much dust was about. They couldn't help kicking the dust up as they walked and some of it got into Anne's throat. 'You'd better have some of your ginger beer to wash it down,' Julian said sympathetically as she started to cough.

Take one PICNIC CARD from your LUNCHBOX. Now go to 10.

As she was looking for her codebook, however, Anne's foot suddenly slipped off the step, causing her to lose her balance. She tumbled all the way to the cellar bottom! Fortunately, there was some sort of thick mat there and she wasn't too hurt but the lid of her lunchbox had come open in the fall. 'Oh, look at my cake,' she sighed, 'it's in tiny pieces all down the steps!' At least her bottle of ginger beer wasn't broken, though, and the cake wasn't completely wasted because Timmy lapped up a lot of it as he went down after her!

Take one PICNIC CARD from your LUNCHBOX. Now go to 42.

'It's a pity we couldn't see who those people were,' remarked Dick as they stepped from the house into the open air again, 'then we could have given a description to the police!' Before they made their way to the lake, George insisted that they stop for a while to have some of their picnic. 'I know everyone can't wait to go and search for that boat,' she said, 'but my tummy can't wait for some food either! All that walking round the house has made me hungry!'

Take one PICNIC CARD from your LUNCHBOX. Now go to 157. (Remember: when there are no picnic cards left in your lunchbox, the game is over and you must start again.)

It was so dark, however, that even *with* the binoculars it was difficult for Julian to work out what the people looked like! 'All I can see is that one is quite a lot shorter than the other,' he whispered, squinting through the lenses. 'I'm afraid their faces are completely in shadow!' Not long after, the people left and The Five began to discuss what they had heard. 'We now know the jewels are in the lake,' George said excitedly, 'so I suggest we go straight back there!' ***Go to 157.***

Timmy suddenly ran off through the trees and so it looked as if they had no choice but to follow his suggestion! But he was in such a hurry that they had trouble keeping up with him. Indeed, by the time they had emerged from the trees and come out on to the moorland again, he had completely disappeared! 'Oh, where is he?' asked George anxiously as she scanned the empty hills. Suddenly, though, she heard a bark in the distance and she quickly looked for her binoculars to try and find him.

Use your BINOCULARS CARD to see if you can spot Timmy by placing exactly over the shape below – then follow the instruction. If you don't have one, go to 264 instead.

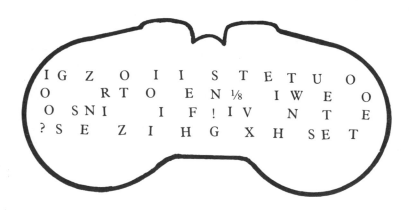

Focusing on the small object, George saw that it wasn't anything special after all – just a lump of wood floating on the water! 'Oh well, at least it saves us going all that way for nothing,' she said as she put the binoculars away again. So Julian steered the raft round a bit, returning to the course he had been on before. *Go to 120.*

135

There was a sudden crack, however, as the sergeant accidentally stepped on a twig and the two people realised there was someone there. They immediately did an about-turn and made a dash for it. By the time the police had come out from their hiding place, it was too late – the two people had disappeared into the night! 'Oh well, at least we managed to recover the jewels,' said the sergeant, not too disappointed. 'And since those two villains think they're still in the lake, I dare say they'll one day return to have another go at getting their hands on them. When they do, we'll be here waiting for them!'

Your adventure wasn't quite successful. If you would like another attempt at solving the mystery, you must start the game again from the beginning. Try choosing a different EQUIP-MENT CARD this time to see if it gives you any more luck.

Arriving at the bridge, they all sat down on the stone wall while they decided which way to go next. 'It looks like we follow the river to the right,' said Julian, noting there was a little footpath on that side. The river-bank was so narrow that they would have to walk along it in single file.

Throw the FAMOUS FIVE DICE to decide who is to walk at the front.

JULIAN thrown	go to 173
DICK thrown	go to 3
GEORGE thrown	go to 124
ANNE thrown	go to 266
TIMMY thrown	go to 204
MYSTERY thrown	go to 223

'I can just see it in the distance!' Dick exclaimed as he suddenly spotted the lake through his binoculars. 'You're right, Julian – we *will* need to take a path across the fields.' So, as soon as he had climbed back down the tree, he led the others to a little stile he had seen further along the river-bank. 'It's still a long way to go,' Dick warned, 'but at least this seems the most direct route!' They had only just crossed the stile when George discovered a map amongst the long grass. 'Someone must have dropped it,' she said and, since it only made the field look untidy, she decided to take it with her.

If you don't already have it, put the MAP CARD into your RUCKSACK. Now go to 163.

138

Focusing his binoculars, Julian suddenly managed to find the radio mast. 'Look, there it is – over to the left!' he said, pointing towards the horizon. When the others had seen it too, they all put their binoculars away again and then started in that direction. They hadn't gone very far when Timmy stopped at a small rock on the ground, giving it some puzzled sniffs. He then tried to roll it over but his nose wasn't strong enough. 'There must be something underneath it!' said Julian as he and Dick gave Timmy a hand. They held one side of the rock up while Anne quickly felt underneath. 'Why, it's a codebook,' she exclaimed. 'Someone must have used the rock to hide it!'

If you don't already have it, put the CODEBOOK CARD into your RUCKSACK. Now go to 90.

139

Anne decided to jump the brook first to encourage the others. If she could make it, they all should! Once they were all safely across, they started to discuss which way to go next. 'If only there was some landmark nearby that we could check on the map,' sighed Dick but then he noticed a huge, sand-coloured building some way to their left. At first they thought it was some sort of factory, but it seemed odd for a factory to be in the middle of nowhere like that. 'Of course – it's the prison,' exclaimed Julian, suddenly realising. 'That's where the escaped prisoner came from!' Now they had something to look up, they all quickly searched for their maps.

Use your MAP CARD to find which square the prison is

in – then follow the instruction. If you don't have one, you'll have to guess which instruction to follow.

If you think E3	go to 79
If you think E4	go to 260
If you think D4	go to 7

140

Their measuring tapes took a while to find since it was so difficult to see but Dick at last managed to feel a round shape. 'Ah, here mine is!' he said, pulling it out of his rucksack. 'Now then – we've got to measure forty metres, haven't we?' ***Go to 226.***

141

Measuring the thirty metres along the wall, they came to a large grandfather clock. 'I wonder what's so special about this,' said Dick. On opening the front, however, they saw that there was a pair of binoculars inside! 'They were probably put there by that prisoner when he originally came to hide the jewels!' Julian said excitedly, guessing that he had used them to look out for intruders.

If you don't already have it, put the BINOCULARS CARD into your RUCKSACK. Now go to 104.

142

'I'd better go first!' said Julian after a while since no one else seemed ready to offer and he slowly led the way down the dark steps. They were about half way to the bottom when Julian suddenly felt something under his feet. Picking it up he saw that it was a guide-book to a stately home. Then he noticed something odd. Someone had drawn an arrow on the photograph at the front, pointing to one of the building's windows. And above the arrow was scribbled some sort of coded message! He immediately told the others to start looking for their codebooks!

*Use your **CODEBOOK CARD** to find out what the message said by decoding the instruction below. If you don't have one, go to 130 instead.*

143

The coded message said that the jewels were hidden in a sunken boat. 'So they must be in the middle of the lake somewhere,' said Dick excitedly. 'That explains why the man said he was going to dive for them!' They were just about to return to the lake when

Julian noticed that the man had dropped something else on the floor. 'Look, it's a measuring tape,' he cried. 'It was probably to help with the search for the jewels!'

If you don't already have it, put the MEASURE CARD into your RUCKSACK. Now go to 157.

144

'Yes, it *does* show a boathouse!' Anne suddenly exclaimed when she had found the lake on her map. Their maps showed that it was about another third of the way round and they all hurried towards the spot, only hoping that it was still there. 'It should be behind those weeping willows,' Anne said anxiously as they came closer and, ducking under the trailing branches, they found that it was! 'Now let's just hope there's a boat inside,' said Julian and he led the way through the rotting door. There wasn't a boat there – but there *was* a small raft, rocking up and down on the shallow water! They were just about to push it on to the lake when Dick noticed a little book wedged between its logs. 'Why, it's a codebook!' he remarked and they decided to take it with them as a spare.

If you don't already have it, put the CODEBOOK CARD into your RUCKSACK. Now go to 57.

145

They put one end of the measuring tape in Timmy's mouth and told him to stay where he was, next to the lily, while they paddled the raft away with the rest of the tape. 'I hope he doesn't move,' said George as she carefully fed the tape out from the spool but Timmy's head remained in exactly the same place above the water. 'Isn't he clever?' remarked Anne. 'I wish I could stay up in the water without moving!' They were soon nearing the fifty-metre mark on their tape and they decided just to guess the rest of the distance so they could call Timmy to join them. They didn't want him to miss out on any of the excitement! *Go to 97.*

146

Pointing her binoculars at the signpost, George could just make out *TO BEACONS VILLAGE – 1 MILE*. 'Hooray, we're nearly there!' she shouted. Before they cut across the fields to the road, however, Julian opened his rucksack to make sure the jewels were still safe. Putting his hand into the polythene bag, he suddenly felt a thin book attached to the bottom with sticky tape. He must have been so intent on admiring the jewels that he hadn't noticed it before! 'Why, it's a codebook,' he exclaimed when he had carefully peeled the tape off. 'We'll hand it in to the police in case it's useful evidence!'

If you don't already have it, put the CODEBOOK CARD into your RUCKSACK. Now go to 180.

Dick directed the helicopter pilot south of the village, eagerly looking below for sign of the lake. It was becoming so dark, however, that it was difficult to see. He asked the pilot if he could switch the underneath lights on but the pilot was worried that it might scare the burglar's accomplices away. 'Perhaps it will be easier with a pair of binoculars,' George suggested and she hurriedly started looking for them in her rucksack.

*Use your **BINOCULARS CARD** to try and spot the lake by placing exactly over the shape below – then follow the instruction. If you don't have one, go to 286 instead.*

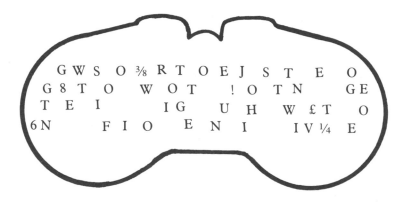

They were just about to take their binoculars out of their rucksacks when they came across a road sign with a black hump. 'That means there's a bridge ahead,' exclaimed Julian, '. . . and so we don't need our binoculars after all!' Now that they knew they were going the right way, they agreed to stop for a quick bite of their picnic. There was a nice piece of grass verge just back from the road and they decided to sit there. This country road was so deserted, however, that they could quite easily have sat in the middle!

*Take one **PICNIC CARD** from your **LUNCHBOX**. Now go to 136.*

'The path becomes wider again soon,' Anne called back to the others as she led the way. So it wasn't long before they were able to walk side by side once more, with room to swing their arms! They hadn't gone much further when they noticed a farmer coming from the other direction and Julian decided it was time to ask the way again. 'Excuse me,' he said, 'but can you tell us where we turn off for Sinister Lake?' The farmer chewed on a piece of straw while he had a think. 'Keep walking along this path until you reach a stile,' he eventually replied with a smile, '– then cut across the fields to your left!' As soon as the farmer had passed, the children looked up the stile on their maps to find out how much further it was.

Use your MAP CARD to find which square the stile is in – then follow the instruction. If you don't have one in your RUCK-SACK, you'll have to guess which instruction to follow.

If you think C2	go to 305
If you think A2	go to 258
If you think B2	go to 88

150

To begin with, they thought they must have miscounted the paces because the binoculars were nowhere to be seen. Or perhaps they had already been taken? But then Timmy started sniffing amongst the rocks at the water's edge. 'Look, he's found them!' cried George as he finally pulled out a small leather case by its strap. Opening the case, the children found that there was another message inside – this time on a scrap of paper. *REG – THESE ARE TO HELP YOU FIND YOUR WAY ON YOUR ESCAPE*, it said. 'So Reg must be the escaped prisoner!' Julian remarked as he took the binoculars with him as evidence for the police.

If you don't already have it, put the BINOCULARS CARD into your RUCKSACK. Now go to 19.

151

They took so long finding their binoculars, however, that by the time they looked through them the two figures had gone! 'Oh no,' cried George, 'they must have suddenly stood up and disappeared behind some trees somewhere. Now we'll never know whether it was that man and woman or not!' So they decided they would just have to keep guessing until they found some other clue. Before they set off again, however, Dick insisted that they sit down for a short while to have some of their picnic. He had been thinking about biting into one of those delicious liver-paste sandwiches for the last quarter of an hour and he couldn't bear it any longer!

Take one PICNIC CARD from your LUNCHBOX. Now go to 64.

Before they could decide who was going to go across the stones first, however, George attracted their attention. 'Hey, look, this first stone has got some writing chalked on to it!' she said, bending down. The others went to have a look at it as well, crouching at George's side. 'It looks like some sort of coded message,' said Julian, noticing the strange letters and symbols. They were so puzzled by them that it took a while for anyone to remember that they had codebooks in their rucksacks!

Use your CODEBOOK CARD to find out what the message said by decoding the instruction below. If you don't have one, go to 253 instead.

The coded message worked out as: *USE THIS KEY FOR MAIN GATE*. At first they were completely puzzled by it, but then Julian suddenly realised which main gate it was talking about. 'It's the one to the prison!' he exclaimed. 'Don't you see, this key must be a duplicate smuggled to the prisoner who escaped!' Dick agreed, saying the prisoner must have dropped it after he got out. 'You know what *that* means, don't you?' asked George as they reached the last of the stones. 'It means that the prisoner must have come this way himself!' **Go to 91.**

The coded message said that Sinister Lake was just on the other side of the wood, about a third of a mile away. 'That means we should reach it soon!' said Anne excitedly, as she put her codebook away again. But the path suddenly ended and they had to make the last of their journey through thick undergrowth. It seemed to take them ages! *Go to 176.*

Since he was the oldest, Julian only thought it right that *he* should enter the house first and he led the way into the dark, dusty interior. Anne suddenly screamed as something touched her face but she realised it was just a large cobweb. She had just got over the shock when she screamed again! 'There's someone watching us from the first floor!' she cried, pointing up the broad staircase. The others couldn't see anything, though, and said she was just imagining it. 'You can just see his outline,' she insisted and told them to look through their binoculars if they didn't believe her!

Use your BINOCULARS CARD to find out if there is anyone up there or not by placing exactly over the shape below – then follow the instruction. If you don't have one, go to 261 instead.

156

Exactly on pace forty, George trod on something on the cellar floor. She could make out the word *CODEBOOK* on the front. 'I wouldn't mind betting it was dropped by that prisoner when he originally came to hide the jewels!' she remarked. They decided to take it with them so they could have a better look at it when they were in daylight again.

If you don't already have it, put the CODEBOOK CARD into your RUCKSACK. Now go to 42.

157

As soon as they were back at the lake, Julian suggested they started looking for some sort of boat to get into the middle. 'It's a good job those people aren't coming back until after dark,' he said, '– it gives us plenty of time!' Anne asked him who he thought the people were and he replied that one of them must have been the person the escaped prisoner meant to hand the message to at the barn. He must have managed to get it to him some other way! 'Anyway, let's try and find this boat,' Julian said. 'I suggest we keep following the edge of the lake round in the hope that we spot one amongst the reeds or something!'

Throw the FAMOUS FIVE DICE to decide who is to lead along the edge of the lake.

JULIAN thrown	go to 107
DICK thrown	go to 219
GEORGE thrown	go to 28
ANNE thrown	go to 83
TIMMY thrown	go to 178
MYSTERY thrown	go to 13

158

The daylight now seemed to be fading by the minute, however, and their maps were difficult to read. 'If we take much longer trying to find out where we are,' said Julian as they all peered at the map's squares, 'we probably won't get back until it's too late anyway!' So they decided to forget about checking their maps and just hope that this *was* the right way for the village. ***Go to 59.***

159

Being the first to find the boundary stone on her map, Anne told the pilot that it was about a couple of miles too far west of the lake and so they *had* flown a bit off course. He immediately made a sharp turn to the left, waiting for two miles to be clocked up on his milometer. 'It should be round about here somewhere,' he said, starting to hover. They all peered into the darkness below, Julian suddenly noticing a reflection of the moon a short way to their right. Only water would make a reflection that clear and so it had to be the lake! ***Go to 110.***

160

They had still to reach the bridge when they spotted three small children coming the other way with fishing nets. Some of their nets were still dripping with water and so it proved that the river must be round any corner now. 'I think even Sherlock Holmes would have been proud of that piece of deduction!' chuckled Dick. ***Go to 136.***

161

Dick hadn't led them far along the narrow footpath when he spotted a man coming the other way. He was carrying a large net in his hand and Dick realised he must be a butterfly collector. They decided it was time to check the way again and so when the man came right up to them they asked if he could help. 'You're looking for Sinister Lake,' the man said, trying to think. 'The best thing you can do is go to the old windmill just across the fields and you should be able to spot it from the top.' He added that they could take a short-cut to the windmill by going through a small gate seventy metres further up the path. To make sure they didn't miss it, they all started looking through their rucksacks for their measuring tapes.

Use your MEASURE CARD to measure this 70 metres – then follow the instruction there. If you don't have a MEASURE CARD in your RUCKSACK, you'll have to guess which instruction to follow.

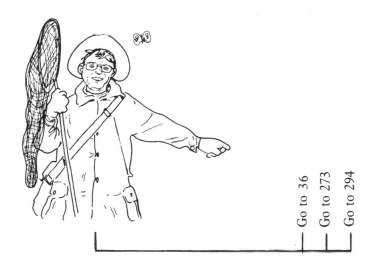

Go to 36
Go to 273
Go to 294

162

'Yes, it *does* point to the lake!' Anne said with glee when she had focused her binoculars on the sign. 'It says that it is another four miles!' She was just about to put her binoculars away again when she noticed a small, black book lying near the bottom of the signpost. Refocusing the binoculars, she saw that it had *SECRET* stamped on the front! 'I wonder what it can be,' they all said excitedly, but there wasn't time to go all the way back to the bridge and walk round. The next thing they knew, however, there was a big splash as Timmy jumped into the water and started paddling across! 'Oh, clever boy, Timmy,' they all cheered as he brought the book back in his mouth, 'but be careful you don't get it wet!' Timmy kept it perfectly dry, though, and the children were soon having a look inside. 'Gosh, it's a secret codebook,' Julian exclaimed, '– and I wouldn't mind betting it belonged to that escaped prisoner!' Since it might be useful evidence to give to the police, they decided to take it with them.

If you don't already have it, put the CODEBOOK CARD into your RUCKSACK. Now go to 233.

163

The countryside soon became a lot more wild, the fields changing to moorland. They seemed to be the only people around but then they suddenly spotted a man and woman coming in the opposite direction. The man had hunched shoulders and a scowling face while the woman wore sunglasses and smoked a cigarette. They didn't really like the look of them and so decided to ignore them, but the man suddenly barred their way and demanded to know where they were going. *Go to 309.*

164

'TO SINISTER LAKE!' George read out with delight as she focused her binoculars on the sign. Now that they were certain they were heading in the right direction, they started to go from stone to stone more quickly. Anne hadn't led them much further, though, when she noticed a map on one of the stones. 'Someone must have dropped it!' she said and, since it seemed to have a lot more detail than their own maps, they decided to take it with them.

If you don't already have it, put the MAP CARD into your RUCKSACK. Now go to 91.

165

'Yes, they *are* herons!' Julian exclaimed as he focused his binoculars on the birds. 'I can even see a fish in one of their beaks!' So they now excitedly set off towards the circle of trees, certain that there must be some water there. And, hopefully, it would be a lake! ***Go to 176.***

166

'I wonder what the point of that was!' George remarked bewilderedly when they had measured the thirty metres but didn't seem to have reached anywhere in particular. But then Anne suddenly felt something under her foot. 'Look, it's a codebook,' she exclaimed, picking it up. 'I bet this is what the note meant the reader to find!' Just in case it contained different codes to their own books, they decided to take it with them.

If you don't already have it, put the CODEBOOK CARD into your RUCKSACK. Now go to 56.

167

They were still waiting for someone to volunteer to lead the way up the stairs when George had an idea. 'I know,' she said, 'we can look at the top through our binoculars. That way, we shall be able to tell whether there's anything to be scared of up there or not!' So they slipped off their rucksacks, starting to feel around inside. 'Why is it that the piece of equipment we want always seems to be at the bottom!' tutted Julian.

Use your BINOCULARS CARD to obtain a better view of the

top of the stairs by placing exactly over the shape below – then follow the instruction. If you don't have one, go to 93 instead.

168

The coded message told them to look under the branches of the weeping-willow a little further round the lake. 'There it is!' cried Julian, pointing to where a large, spindly tree bent over the edge of the water. Running up to it, they found that there was a small raft underneath, sitting on the mud! ***Go to 95.***

169

Exactly on pace one hundred, they found the binoculars – hidden in an old biscuit tin amongst the reeds – but they were just an ordinary pair after all! 'Oh well, we might as well take them anyway,' said George, 'there's no point in just leaving them here.' As soon as she had put them in her rucksack, they all returned to the raft, taking turns to paddle it towards the middle.

If you don't already have it, put the BINOCULARS CARD into your RUCKSACK. Now go to 97.

Julian told George there was no point in searching for her binoculars, though, because the letters on the signpost would be too dark to make out by now anyway. George had a look at the signpost again. Julian was right – even the white parts didn't show up that well! Anne suddenly noticed some lights twinkling a mile or so further up the road, however, and so it looked as if the village *was* that way, after all! As they followed the road along, George finished off her sandwiches to make her lunchbox easier to carry.

Take one PICNIC CARD from your LUNCHBOX. Now go to 180. (Remember: when there are no picnic cards left in your lunchbox, the game is over and you must start again.)

171

Focusing her binoculars, George saw that there *was* someone approaching between the trees. In fact, two people – and obviously the same two people that had been in the mansion! Before she had quite made out their faces, though, she put her binoculars away again so that they wouldn't get damaged if she had to help arrest them! *Go to 247.*

172

'Yes, there it is!' cried Anne as she suddenly spotted the pump's little black shape at the far end of the village. Putting their binoculars away again, they all hurried towards it. As they got nearer to the pump, they noticed a little lane beside it, leading across the fields. 'That must be the turning the porter told us to take,' Julian said. Before they did, though, they decided to see if the pump still worked. 'Yes, it does!' exclaimed Dick as they all took it in turns to drink its deliciously cool water. *Go to 111.*

Julian hadn't led them far along the river-bank when he noticed a strange-looking bundle hidden amongst the reeds. Opening it up, they found that it was someone's clothes! They wondered why *BLEAKMOORS* was stamped all over them but then Dick remembered that that was the name of the nearby prison. 'They must have belonged to the escaped prisoner,' he told the others excitedly, 'and he changed them for something less noticeable.' At that moment, a scrap of paper fell from one of the pockets and they saw that there was a message on it. Unfortunately, it was in code and so they started to look for their codebooks to see if they could help.

Use your CODEBOOK CARD to find out what the message said by decoding the instruction below. If you don't have one in your RUCKSACK, go to 99 instead.

When Julian tried to take off his rucksack to look for his binoculars, however, he over-balanced and nearly slipped off the stepping-stone into the marsh! George was having trouble with her rucksack, too, and so Julian said they had better forget about trying to read the sign. Finally, they reached the other end of the stones and to celebrate Anne suggested they sit down for a while so they could have a quick bite of their picnic.

Take one PICNIC CARD from your LUNCHBOX. Now go to 91.

175

Finally reaching pace 130, they saw that there was a thin plank across the brook. 'I much prefer this to *jumping* across,' said Anne as she carefully stepped on. She had had this horrible vision of not quite jumping far enough and falling back into the dirty water! 'Yes, I *much* prefer it!' she repeated as she safely reached the other side. *Go to 79.*

176

They at last heard some ducks quacking ahead and, moments later, they came to a large expanse of water bordered by willows. With its eerie, rippling sound and strange green colour, it could only be Sinister Lake! Anne was just saying what a spooky place it was when she suddenly noticed a large, derelict house just visible through the trees at the other end. 'Perhaps it was once a rich person's mansion and this lake was part of the estate,' said Dick. Thinking that the building was the most likely hiding place for the jewels, Julian suggested that they go and explore it first. So they all hurried round the lake, finally reaching the mansion's front door. 'Who's going to go in first?' asked George, with a bit of a shiver.

Throw the FAMOUS FIVE DICE to find out.

JULIAN thrown	go to 155
DICK thrown	go to 207
GEORGE thrown	go to 25
ANNE thrown	go to 9
TIMMY thrown	go to 299
MYSTERY thrown	go to 54

177

'Here the windmill is,' said Anne, pointing to the middle of her map as she held it up to the light. 'That means we must be facing roughly north!' They were putting their maps away again when Timmy started sniffing at something in a dark corner. 'If that's a bone,' George lectured him sternly, 'you can just leave it where it is – because it's probably been lying there for years!' Timmy took no notice, though, dragging whatever it was towards them. To begin with they did think it was a bone, but as the object became clearer they realised it was a pair of binoculars! 'Well done, Timmy,' they all broke into a chuckle, patting him on the head. 'We'll take them with us as a spare!'

If you don't already have it, put the BINOCULARS CARD into your RUCKSACK. Now go to 117.

Timmy had only led them a short way round the edge of the lake when they came to a *NO BOATING* sign. It didn't look a very good sign, however – most of the letters being crooked! 'I bet it was just put there by that prisoner to stop people going too close to the jewels!' said Dick. Bending nearer, he noticed that there was a tiny message scribbled in the corner. 'I think it's in some sort of code,' he said and he suggested they take out their codebooks to see if they could help.

Use your CODEBOOK CARD to find out what the message said by decoding the instruction below. If you don't have one, go to 14 instead.

179

While they were on their knees looking for their codebooks, however, Anne suddenly slipped, causing the raft to rock danger-ously. Fortunately, they were finally able to steady it again but the end of the raft had become drenched with water and the message had washed away! That wasn't the only disaster. In the panic, George's lunchbox had gone over the edge. Although she was just able to reach it before it sank, quite a lot of water had leaked in and most of her sandwiches were now ruined. They would just have to be thrown out for the ducks!

Take one PICNIC CARD from your LUNCHBOX. Now go to 120.

180

Finally reaching the village, they immediately made their way to the police station. On seeing them enter, the sergeant gave another of his long sighs but his expression soon changed when they emptied the jewels on to his desk! 'There'll be a big reward for this!' he told them delightedly – but The Five were more concerned that he should hear about the two people at the mansion and how they had said that they would be back at the lake after dark. 'So that's why the escaped prisoner had such a big smile on his face!' the sergeant remarked. He explained to them that he had been rearrested several hours ago but for some reason he hadn't seemed all that unhappy about it. It was obvious now why . . . because he had managed to get in touch with his accomplices about the jewels! The sergeant then started to summon a couple of his men, telling the children to prepare themselves for another trip to the lake; this time, by police helicopter! *Go to 32.*

They finally decided on Dick's idea – to walk along to the village railway station and ask someone there. 'Excuse me,' said Dick when they had found a porter sweeping the platform, 'but can you tell us the way to Sinister Lake?' The porter put down his broom before answering. 'Well, it's a fair way from here,' he replied, lifting his cap to scratch his head, 'but you'll be heading in the right direction if you take the little turning just after the village pump.' When they were back outside the station, however, they wondered which way the pump was – for they couldn't spot it anywhere. 'Perhaps it will be easier with our binoculars,' Julian suggested suddenly and so they all started looking through their rucksacks for them.

Do you have a pair of BINOCULARS in your RUCKSACK? If so, use them to try and find the village pump by placing exactly over the shape below – then follow the instruction. (Remember to put the CARD back in your RUCKSACK afterwards.) If you don't have a BINOCULARS CARD in your RUCKSACK, go to 203 instead.

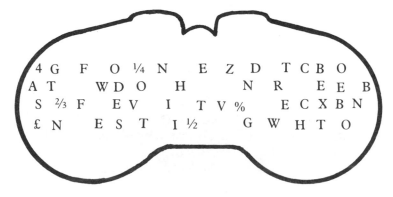

```
4 G   F   O  ¼ N    E   Z  D   T C B  O
A T      W D  O     H        N   R     E E   B
S ⅔ F   E V    I   T V %        E  C X B N
£  N   E  S  T    I ½        G  W  H  T  O
```

182

Julian's codebook seemed to be right at the bottom of his rucksack and he took everything else out so he could find it more easily. First he put his anorak on the wall, then his binoculars, then his map. When he took out his measuring tape, however, he wasn't really concentrating and he rested it just a bit too near to the wall's edge. The next thing he knew, there was a loud *plop* as it dropped into the river below! They all ran down to see if they could rescue it but the water proved far too deep for paddling. 'We'll just have to leave it,' said Julian reluctantly, and they had wasted so much time that they decided to leave the decoding of the message as well.

If you have it, remove the MEASURE CARD from your RUCKSACK. Now go to 19.

183

'We must be round here somewhere,' said Dick, when he had found Rabbit Hill on his map. They felt a lot better now they knew where they were and all agreed that they owed Timmy an apology. 'He wasn't interested in the rabbits after all,' said George guiltily as she patted him on the head, 'but just helping us out.' Timmy's face was so expressionless that it was difficult to tell whether this had been his real reason or not! *Go to 64.*

Timmy decided that he was to go first across the stones, leading the way from one to the next. After about a quarter of an hour they finally reached the other end, stepping on to firm ground again. They hadn't left the marsh far behind them when Dick spotted a tall stone on a nearby hill. 'It's probably a boundary marker,' said Julian, and he suggested they look it up on their maps as a rough guide to where they were.

Use your MAP CARD to find which square the tall stone is in – then follow the instruction. If you don't have one, you'll have to guess which instruction to follow.

If you think A3	go to 103
If you think A4	go to 91
If you think B3	go to 38

'*TO REACH SINISTER LAKE* . . .' they all started to read again when they had decoded the rest of the message, '. . . *HEAD TOWARDS THE BOUNDARY STONE.*' To begin with they didn't know what it was talking about, but then George noticed a tall pillar of rock on a hill in the distance. 'It must be that,' she said. 'The message probably means that the lake is somewhere on the way!' *Go to 24.*

'Now be very careful where you tread,' warned Dick when he had nearly reached the forty-metre mark on his measuring tape. He stretched out his foot, suddenly feeling a large hole in front of them. 'Here it is!' he said and they now shouted back to Julian, who had been holding the tape's other end. As soon as he had joined them, they all carefully felt their way round the edge of the hole. 'Gosh, it could have caused a nasty accident!' said Anne, realising how big it was. *Go to 104.*

187

'I've never known such a long cellar!' remarked Dick as they were finally coming up to the last of the forty paces. It brought them to a large box on the floor and they opened the lid to feel what was inside. 'It's something rubbery,' said Julian bewilderedly – and then he suddenly realised it was a wet-suit! 'It must have been brought here by that prisoner when he originally came to hide the jewels,' he told them, '– but what would he want a wet-suit for?' The others couldn't work it out either! *Go to 42.*

188

They carefully moved their binoculars round, scrutinising every nook and cranny along the lake. 'There could be something *there*!' George suddenly shouted, pointing to a large hole in the reeds some way to their left. Running up to it, they found that the hole had been made by a small raft which was hidden in the reeds! 'That's just as good as any boat!' they all exclaimed with delight. *Go to 57.*

189

They were still trying to decide who was to do the paddling when George noticed that the branch had a message carved on it. *FOR PAIR OF BINOCULARS*, it read, *TURN LEFT AND THEN WALK 100 PACES ROUND LAKE*. Dick said they shouldn't waste their time since they already had binoculars with them but George said they might be a special pair for seeing through the water. So they went back to where they had picked up the branch and then started to count the hundred paces.

Use your MEASURE CARD to count the 100 paces yourself –
then follow the instruction there. If you don't have one, you'll
have to guess which instruction to follow.

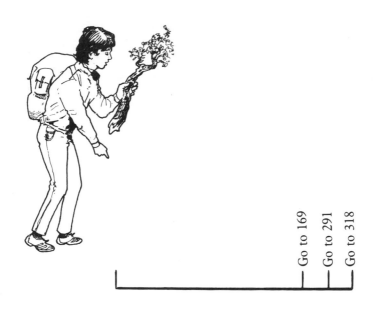

Go to 169
Go to 291
Go to 318

190

Trampling across the thick, marshy undergrowth between the lake and the chimney, they finally reached the seventy-metre mark on their tapes. They wondered what they were supposed to find there but then Dick felt something wobble under his feet. 'We must be standing on something,' he said and they started to kick open a hole in the leafy tangle to see what it was. 'Look, it's a small raft!' exclaimed George. 'Exactly what we wanted!' **Go to 95.**

191

They had only counted 40 of the 110 paces, however, when they suddenly heard two pairs of footsteps coming towards the lake and someone talking. They all immediately rushed for cover behind a nearby group of trees, crouching down. 'We obviously only just got here in time!' the sergeant whispered excitedly. ***Go to 247.***

192

'Yes, there it is – straight ahead!' exclaimed George as she spotted the bridge through her binoculars. It was still a good half mile off, however, and so as soon as they had put their binoculars back in their rucksacks they started walking again. 'What a peaceful road this is,' said Anne, realising that they hadn't seen so much as one vehicle on it yet. In fact, the only 'traffic' at all had been a herd of cows, waddling down the road's centre! ***Go to 136.***

193

They all followed Timmy until the footpath broadened out again and they could walk side by side once more. 'I wonder which way we go now,' Julian said when the path finally ended at some fields. But then Anne suddenly spotted a little green signpost in the distance. 'Perhaps that will point to the lake!' she remarked. Dick said that it might point somewhere else, though, and it would be a pity to go all that way if it did. 'If only we had some means of reading it from here,' he sighed – but then he realised that they had! They could use their binoculars!

Use your BINOCULARS CARD to read what the signpost says

by placing exactly over the shape below – then follow the instruction. If you don't have one in your RUCKSACK, go to 34 instead.

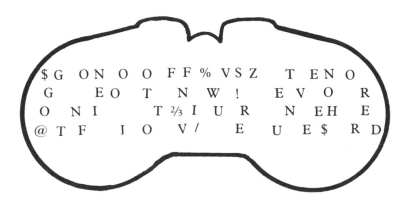

```
$ G  ON O  O  F F % V S Z    T  EN O
  G     E O T   N W  !    E V  O   R
  O  N I      T ⅔ I  U R    N  EH  E
@ T  F    I O  V /    E    U  E $   R D
```

194

By the time they had all found their binoculars, however, the sky was empty. The ducks must have suddenly landed while they weren't looking! 'How silly we are,' exclaimed Julian. 'We should have made sure that one of us kept an eye on them!' At least they knew *roughly* which way the ducks had gone, though, and so they headed in that direction themselves. George thought if she held out one of her sandwiches she might attract the ducks back again. But she soon realised how silly the idea was and just ate the sandwich herself!

Take one PICNIC CARD from your LUNCHBOX. Now go to 24.

195

Just as they were about to look through their binoculars, they heard a distant bark. 'Look, there Timmy is,' George cried, pointing to her right, '– we don't need our binoculars after all!' They all ran up to him, George giving him a bit of a ticking-off for rushing ahead. 'But at least you were considerate enough to bark,' she added – and so she wasn't that cross. She might have been, though, if she had realised what had happened because of Timmy! She had been so anxious to take out her binoculars at the bank, that she had unknowingly dropped her map there!

If you have it, remove the MAP CARD from your RUCKSACK. Now go to 79.

196
They had finally got round to opening their maps when they heard a noise from one of the mansion's broken windows above. 'There's someone inside!' Anne exclaimed as they all jumped up in fright. They were just beginning to let their imaginations run away with them – thinking it might be a previous owner's ghost climbing the stairs or old butlers roaming the halls – when Julian saw what had caused it. 'Look, it's just a wood pigeon pecking around on that ledge up there!' he laughed with relief. *Go to 129.*

197
'You're right, Anne,' Julian exclaimed as he directed his binoculars at where she was pointing, 'there *is* someone there!' When he focused them properly, however, he saw that it was just a suit of armour standing against the wall. 'What idiots we both are!' he chuckled with Anne as he put his binoculars away again. A second or two later, it was George's turn to give a sudden scream. 'There's something grabbing hold of my feet!' she yelled. Bending down to

fight it off, however, she saw that she had just got tangled up in an old measuring tape! 'We might as well take it with us as a spare,' said Dick, beginning to wind it into its spool.

If you don't already have it, put the MEASURE CARD into your RUCKSACK. Now go to 104.

198

Since it looked as if no one else would, *Dick* eventually offered to go down the cellar steps first! He was just putting his foot on the last step when he noticed there was a message written on it in a special paint that glowed in the dark. *WALK 40 PACES STRAIGHT AHEAD*, it read. As soon as the others had joined him at the bottom of the stairs, they all started to count the forty paces!

Use your MEASURE CARD to count the 40 paces yourself – then follow the instruction there. If you don't have one, you'll have to guess which instruction to follow.

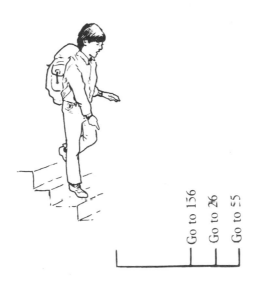

Go to 156

Go to 26

Go to 55

The coded message said that the jewels were hidden three metres under. 'It must have been written by the thief as a clue to his friends,' said Julian, '– but it doesn't really help much. We don't know whether it means three metres under the floor, under the roof or what!' *Go to 56.*

When they had found the sundial in the grounds they suddenly realised they didn't know which direction to measure the sixty metres. But then Anne noticed that a little arrow had been chalked on it and they guessed it must be that way. They were right – because exactly at the sixty-metre mark on their tapes they found a large box under a bush! 'Look, there's a diving-suit inside,' exclaimed Dick, '– that must mean that the jewels are quite deep down in the lake!' They also found a codebook in the box and they decided to take it with them as evidence for the police. Going to the police station could come later, though. First of all, they meant to search the lake for the jewels themselves!

If you don't already have it, put the CODEBOOK CARD into your RUCKSACK. Now go to 157.

201

'Oh, I've just thought of something,' said Dick as he was taking his measuring tape out, 'how are we going to keep one end of the tape here at the buoy while we paddle away with the other?' They all scratched their heads for a moment but then Julian suddenly had a clever idea. 'I know,' he said, 'we can measure the length of the raft and then work out how many lengths make fifty metres. We should then be able to estimate the distance!' There were about twenty-five raft lengths in fifty metres, and so that was the number of lengths they had to paddle. *Go to 97.*

202

George sat next to the pilot, pointing the way as the helicopter rose higher and higher. Anne decided to follow their route on her map just in case George needed any help. So as soon as she had taken it out of her rucksack, she first of all started looking for the police station!

Use your MAP CARD to find which square the police station is in – then follow the instruction. If you don't have one, you'll have to guess which instruction to follow.

If you think A1	go to 121
If you think B1	go to 265
If you think C1	go to 86

203

Just as they were about to use their binoculars, however, they heard a voice from behind. It was the porter, who had come running out of the station after them. 'How silly of me,' he replied, 'I was forgetting you were strangers here and wouldn't know where the pump was. Just go straight down this road here to the other end of the village.' When they had found the pump and the little turning next to it, George suggested having some of their picnic before continuing. 'Okay,' agreed Julian, '– but not too much because we've got a long way to go yet!'

Take one PICNIC CARD from your LUNCHBOX. Now go to 111.

204

Timmy had led them quite a way along the river-bank when he suddenly stopped and pricked up his ears. 'What is it, Timmy – what can you hear?' George asked, but it wasn't long before the children could hear it too. It was a loud hissing noise. 'It sounds like a small waterfall,' said Dick excitedly and as they turned the next corner they found that's exactly what it was. Julian thought it was probably just about large enough to be shown on the map and he suggested looking it up to find out roughly where they were.

Use your MAP CARD to find which square the small waterfall is in (look carefully!) – then follow the instruction. If you don't

have one in your RUCKSACK, you'll have to guess which instruction to follow.

If you think E1	go to 242
If you think D2	go to 232
If you think D3	go to 19

205

Just as the others were about to use their binoculars, however, Dick moved a few paces to his left. 'Look, there the radio mast is!' he shouted, pointing towards the horizon. 'It was hidden by that tree over there!' When the others moved over to join him, they were also suddenly able to see it and they were soon setting off in that direction. *Go to 90.*

206

On the way to the ridge, Dick tried to puzzle out where he had seen that man's face before but then he suddenly remembered – it was in a framed photograph in Mrs Taggart's farmhouse. He must have been her son! Dick recalled the old woman saying that he was not very nice and The Five started to worry that he might have lied to them about the lake. When they finally reached the ridge, they found that he *had* – for there was not a lake in sight! 'What a mean trick,' exclaimed Julian. 'We must have been going the right way after all!' So they were just going to have to find their way back again but they had made such a large detour that they weren't sure which route to take. They all had a think for a moment, each coming up with a different suggestion.

Throw the FAMOUS FIVE DICE to decide whose suggestion they should follow.

JULIAN thrown	go to 287
DICK thrown	go to 6
GEORGE thrown	go to 37
ANNE thrown	go to 125
TIMMY thrown	go to 114
MYSTERY thrown	go to 243

207

'Be careful how you tread,' Dick called back as he led the way across the creaking floor, 'it's really dark in here!' They could just make out the silhouette of a large candelabra and several broken chairs. Suddenly, Anne gave a loud scream as she saw a face staring at her! 'Oh, it's just a mirror!' she laughed, her heart still pounding. She was about to move on when she noticed that someone had written a message on the mirror with a wax crayon. *MEASURE 30 METRES ALONG THE WALL*, it read. No sooner had she told the others than they all started looking for their measuring tapes!

Use your MEASURE CARD to measure 30 metres from the

mirror – then follow the instruction there. If you don't have one,
you'll have to guess which instruction to follow.

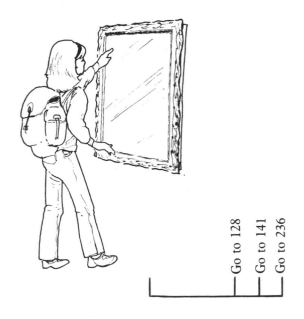

Go to 128
Go to 141
Go to 236

208

There must have been another candle on the floor, however,
because Anne suddenly slipped on something and sent the one in
her hand flying! 'Oh no, we'll never find it now,' she said as they
were suddenly in complete darkness again. They couldn't even find
the one that had done the mischief either – because it seemed to
have rolled away somewhere. And there was *more* bad news. When
she had slipped, Anne had dropped her lunchbox and it now made a
rattling noise as she picked it up again. Her bottle of ginger beer had
obviously broken!

Take one PICNIC CARD from your LUNCHBOX. Now go to
269.

209

Timmy became so bored waiting for them to do the measuring, however, that he wandered off towards a small wooden fishing shelter a little further round the lake. Suddenly, he started barking back at them from inside! 'He must have hurt himself or something!' cried George with alarm and so they left the measuring for the moment, running towards the hut themselves. When they got inside, however, they saw that Timmy had a great big smile on his face and next to him was a small raft! 'Well done, Timmy,' George cried with relief and joy, and she gave him a large piece of her cake as a reward!

Take one PICNIC CARD from your LUNCHBOX. Now go to 95.

210

They eventually agreed on Anne's suggestion, following her to a small hill not far from the lake. 'With any luck, we should be able to *see* the village from up there,' she said. When they reached the top of the hill, however, they weren't sure whether it was the village they could make out in the distance or not. Perhaps it was just several farmhouses! 'I know,' exclaimed George, 'we can look through our binoculars!'

Use your BINOCULARS CARD to find out whether or not it's

the village they can see by placing exactly over the shape below – then follow the instruction. If you don't have one, go to 316 instead.

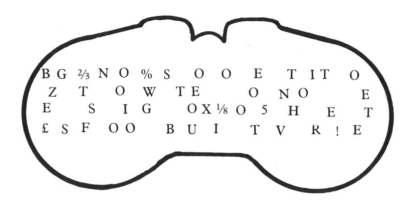

B G ⅔ N O % S O O E T IT O
Z T O W TE   O N O   E
E   S   I G   O X ⅛ O 5 H   E   T
£ S F OO   B U I   T V   R ! E

211

While they were still searching for their maps, however, Timmy suddenly started barking! 'What is it, boy?' the pilot asked but then he noticed that Timmy's nose was pointing to a large white circle some distance to their left. It could only be the lake, shimmering in the moonlight! *Go to 110.*

212

'I can't see a little turning anywhere,' said Julian when they had counted out the hundred paces. They were just beginning to think that the sergeant had played a trick on them when Dick suddenly realised something. 'Of course,' he exclaimed, 'the sergeant's paces will be a lot bigger than ours! So we had better keep going for a bit.' Sure enough, thirty or so paces more and they arrived at the turning. 'I think we all owe the sergeant an apology!' Dick laughed. *Go to 111.*

213

Dick was still trying to spot the lake through his binoculars when he heard someone shout at him from below. 'I would be careful of that tree if I were you,' the voice called. 'It might not look it but it's almost completely rotten!' Dick immediately started to climb down again, therefore, soon reaching the bottom. He saw that the voice belonged to a fisherman who had been passing along the bank. 'Where were you looking for?' the fisherman asked them and, when Julian told him, 'Sinister Lake,' he led them along the river-bank to a small footpath that cut across the fields. 'It's still a fair way, mind,' he warned, 'but at least that will point you in the general direction!' *Go to 163.*

214

'Yes, it does point to the lake!' George said delightedly when she had focused her binoculars. The others focused their binoculars on the signpost too, giving a similar yell of delight. Now knowing that it wouldn't be a wasted journey, they therefore hurried in its direction. When they finally reached the signpost, Dick noticed a large sheet of paper on the grass at the bottom. 'Look, someone's left their map here,' he remarked, picking it up. Since it seemed to have more detail than their own maps, they decided to take it with them.

If you don't already have it, put the MAP CARD into your RUCKSACK. Now go to 224.

215

Before they left the hill, they decided to have a brief sit down for some of their picnic. Timmy watched the rabbits all around him, looking rather sad that he wasn't allowed to chase them. 'Never mind,' said Anne, giving him a big slice of her cherry cake, 'perhaps this will make up for it.' On his first bite, a bit of a smile came back. On the second, he looked quite cheerful. And by the time he had finished, he didn't seem to care whether there were hundreds of rabbits or not!

Take one PICNIC CARD from your LUNCHBOX. Now go to 64.

George had nearly led them to the other end of the stepping-stones when she suddenly stopped to bend down. 'Look, someone's dropped a large key on this stone,' she said, picking it up. Turning it over, she noticed that there were several letters and symbols scratched on to the other side. To begin with, she wondered what they were but then she realised that it must be a coded message of some sort. She twisted round to show the others, telling them to take out their codebooks!

Use your CODEBOOK CARD to find out what the message said by decoding the instruction below. If you don't have one, go to 115 instead.

The print in their codebooks was so small, however, that it was impossible to read in the little light available. 'It's a pity we didn't think to bring our torches along,' remarked Dick with an annoyed tut at himself. He then suggested taking the bag outside to decode the message there but Julian said it would waste too much time. 'It's already four in the afternoon,' he told Dick, 'and we don't even know where to start looking for the jewels yet!' So they decided to put their codebooks away again but it was so dark that Julian grabbed his rucksack by the wrong end. His map slipped quietly to the floor, lying unnoticed amongst the dust!

If you have it, remove the MAP CARD from your RUCKSACK. Now go to 10.

218
George was in such a hurry to find her binoculars for Dick that she accidentally pulled out her measuring tape. It bounced on the floor and then started to roll along the landing! 'Oh no, it's going towards the edge!' she cried but before they could run after it, it had dropped over. 'You'll just have to forget about it,' Anne told her sympathetically, as they all stared over the banister. 'You'll never find it again in that darkness!' So they returned to the window, everyone resuming the search for their binoculars.

If you have it, remove the MEASURE CARD from your RUCKSACK. Now go to 56.

219
'What do we do if there isn't a boat anywhere?' Dick asked anxiously as he led the way. The others didn't know, only praying there would be! They had only gone a little further when Julian noticed that someone had carved a message into a tree just back from the lake. *WALK 70 METRES TOWARDS TALL CHIMNEY*, it read. They wondered what tall chimney it was talking about but then Anne noticed that they could just see one of the chimneys of the mansion above the trees. They immediately started looking for their measuring tapes!

Use your MEASURE CARD to measure these 70 metres from

the tree – then follow the instruction there. If you don't have one, you'll have to guess which instruction to follow.

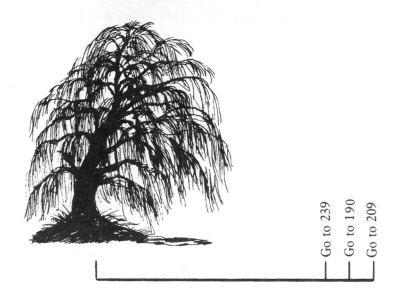

Go to 239
Go to 190
Go to 209

220

Dick said it would make more sense, though, to leave looking up the railway station until they *got* there. Otherwise, they might forget which end of the village it was and have to look it up a second time anyway! So they all fastened their rucksacks up again, leaving their maps inside. As they continued to follow the railway line, George threw out the remainder of her sandwiches for the birds to make her lunchbox lighter.

Take one PICNIC CARD from your LUNCHBOX. Now go to 180.

221

As soon as George had found her binoculars, she passed them forward to Dick over his shoulder. 'Thanks,' he said and hurriedly pointed them through the open door at his side. After searching round for a while, he suddenly spotted the lake, just shimmering a little in the moonlight. 'There it is!' he cried and the pilot immediately started to swoop down towards it. *Go to 110.*

222

'Here it is!' exclaimed Dick, pointing to a little building marked *The Three Shepherds* on his map. Just as they were setting off for the inn, however, the gardener called after them. 'You might like to take this with you,' he shouted, waving a measuring tape in the air. 'I've just found it in the grass and it might well come in useful on your journey.' Although they each had a measuring tape with them, the children thought there was no harm in carrying a spare and so Julian gratefully ran back for it.

If you don't already have it, put the MEASURE CARD into your RUCKSACK. Now go to 111.

223

They had still to make up their minds who was to go first along the river-bank when Dick noticed that there was some sort of message scratched on to the bridge. 'It looks as if it's in code,' he said, studying the strange letters and symbols. They were so busy trying to guess what it could mean that they completely forgot that they had codebooks with them. Then Anne suddenly remembered! 'Of course, our codebooks,' she exclaimed, 'maybe they'll be able to help!' So they all quickly rested their rucksacks on the wall so they could start looking for them.

Use your CODEBOOK CARD to find out what the message meant by decoding the instruction below. If you don't have one in your RUCKSACK, go to 182 instead.

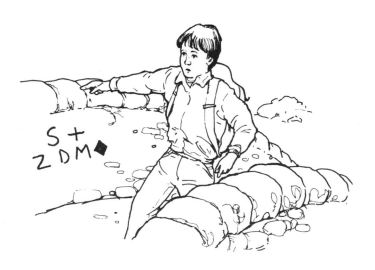

They crossed field after field but the lake still wasn't anywhere in sight. While they had a brief rest amongst some poppies, Dick had another look at that mysterious note he had received back at the barn. He hadn't noticed before but scribbled on the other side were some very faint letters and symbols. 'It looks like some sort of code,' said Julian excitedly. He then suggested taking out their codebooks to see if they could work out what it meant.

Use your CODEBOOK CARD to find out what the scribble said

by decoding the instruction below. If you don't have one in your RUCKSACK, go to 100 instead.

225

George was so impatient to find her measuring tape that she turned her rucksack right over, emptying everything on to the ground. Suddenly, though, there was a strong gust of wind and it blew her map back towards the marshy area. 'Quick, stop it before it's too late!' she shouted to the others, but there was nothing they could do about it. Seconds later, it was lying right in the middle of a large wet patch, impossible to reach! 'Perhaps we had better move away from here before we have any more accidents,' said Julian, and so they decided just to forget about looking for the hiding place.

If you have it, remove the MAP CARD from your RUCKSACK. Now go to 91.

226

George was left by the message holding the measure's spool while the others pulled out the tape. 'Make sure you don't move!' Dick called back as they walked further and further away. Being all on her own soon started to make her nervous, however, and she couldn't help edging in their direction. Suddenly, there was a loud crash as Anne tripped on the edge of the hole! Fortunately, she wasn't hurt but her lunchbox had come open in the fall and some of her sandwiches were now covered in dust. 'They'll just have to be thrown away,' said Julian, still not sure why the hole was at thirty metres instead of forty. George had a fair idea, of course, but she was keeping absolutely quiet about it!

Take one PICNIC CARD from your LUNCHBOX. Now go to 104.

227

Focusing her binoculars on the message, George read it out to the others. *'JEWELS ARE NOT DOWN HERE – HA, HA, HA!'* she read. She guessed that it had been written by the prisoner when he originally came to hide the jewels. 'It's obviously his idea of a little joke,' she remarked sourly, not finding it at all funny! ***Go to 269.***

228

The coded message *did* say where a boat was hidden. Well, not a boat exactly – a raft! It said that it could be found amongst the group of bulrushes. 'Look, there they are!' exclaimed Dick, pointing to a mass of furry brown tops a little further along. Trampling some of the bulrushes aside, they eventually uncovered the raft – a number of logs fastened together – resting on the mud. Lying next to the raft was a small leather case in a polythene bag. Curious to know what was inside, they opened the lid of the case. 'It's a pair of binoculars!' remarked Julian with surprise. 'I wonder what these were intended for?' Whatever it was, they decided to take them with them as a spare!

If you don't already have it, put the BINOCULARS CARD into your RUCKSACK. Now go to 57.

229

Since they were in such a hurry, they quickly decided on Julian's suggestion and he led them through the trees and towards a small river in the distance. 'I'm sure this is the river that runs just outside the village,' he told them as they eventually reached it. Some time later, they passed a little island in the middle and they decided to look it up on their maps just to check this was the *right* river.

Use your MAP CARD to find which square the river-island is in – then follow the instruction. If you don't have one, you'll have to guess which instruction to follow.

If you think E2	go to 96
If you think D2	go to 319
If you think D3	go to 158

The children were still looking for their maps when the moon suddenly came out and started shimmering on a large circle of water to their left. 'It must be the lake!' the sergeant said joyfully. 'You children won't need your maps after all!' As the helicopter made a sharp turn towards the lake, Julian handed round the remainder of his sandwiches to celebrate.

Take one PICNIC CARD from your LUNCHBOX. Now go to 110.

They finally agreed on Julian's idea – which was to ask a gardener working on the village green. He was pushing a heavy roller up and down to level the ground. 'Excuse me,' said Julian as they all hurried up to him, 'but can you tell us the way to Sinister Lake?' The gardener wiped his damp forehead with a handkerchief before answering. 'Well, let me see . . .,' he replied. 'Yes, you want to turn right just after the village inn. That will point you in the general direction.' Thanking him for his trouble, The Five then started to look through their rucksacks for their maps so they could find out where the inn was.

Do you have a MAP in your RUCKSACK? If so, use it to find which square the village inn is in – then follow the instruction. (Remember to put it back in your RUCKSACK afterwards.) If you don't have a MAP CARD in your RUCKSACK, you'll have to guess which instruction to follow.

If you think D1	go to 111
If you think C1	go to 257
If you think B1	go to 222

232

When they had found the waterfall on their maps, they decided to have a short rest before continuing on their way. George let Timmy have a quick paddle but she told him to keep near the bank in case he was dragged near the edge by the strong current. 'Waterfalls might look a lot of fun,' she warned him, 'but they can be quite dangerous!' *Go to 19.*

233

They had walked quite a distance further along the river-bank when they noticed a fisherman sitting by his rod. Julian decided to check the way again and so told him that they were looking for Sinister Lake. 'Not a place I would go to myself,' the fisherman replied with a shiver, '– even if it had the best fishing in the world! You see, several fishermen – friends of mine – have had horrible experiences there. But, if you must go, you should take the little footpath across the fields sixty metres further along.' To make sure they didn't walk right past it, the children immediately started looking for their measuring tapes.

Use your MEASURE CARD to measure this 60 metres from the

fisherman – then follow the instruction there. If you don't have one in your RUCKSACK, you'll have to guess which instruction to follow.

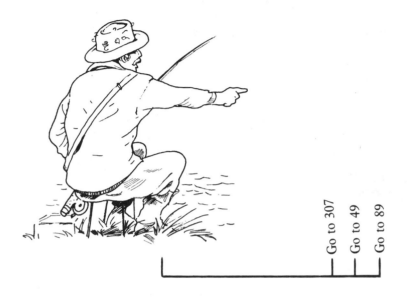

Go to 307

Go to 49

Go to 89

234

'Gosh, we're miles out of our way!' said George when they had found the mire on their maps. The map showed that there was a narrow track nearby that led back in the direction they wanted, however, and they decided to make for that. They had only gone a short way along the track when Timmy started sniffing amongst the grass at the edge. Then he started to dig away at the soil with his paws. The others thought he had just found an old bone but then he uncovered a round, leather case. 'Why, it's a measuring tape!' Julian exclaimed. When they pulled it out, they found that it was a lot longer than the ones they had and so they took it with them in case it had some use.

If you don't already have it, put the MEASURE CARD into your RUCKSACK. Now go to 64.

'They're flying towards those trees over there!' George exclaimed as the ducks became much bigger through their binoculars. They had only flown a short way beyond the trees when they started to come down. 'That must be where the lake is!' the children all shouted for joy as they made in the same direction themselves. *Go to 24.*

236
They had only measured twenty-three metres, however, when the wall ended! 'Perhaps it meant thirty metres the other way?' suggested George. But the mirror had been even nearer the other end and so that didn't make any sense either. 'It was obviously a practical joke to trick intruders into thinking they had found the jewels when they hadn't!' said Julian disappointedly. To make themselves feel a bit better, they decided to sit down on an old chest and have a little of their cake before resuming their search.

Take one PICNIC CARD from your LUNCHBOX. Now go to 104.

237
'Oh, I'll go first!' George offered eventually, pretending to be much braver than she was. They had just reached the last of the stairs when Anne noticed there was a message chalked on it. 'I think it's in some sort of code,' she said, bending down to have a better look. It wasn't

long before they were all excitedly feeling through their rucksacks for their codebooks!

Use your CODEBOOK CARD to find out what the message said by decoding the instruction below. If you don't have one, go to 254 instead.

S + P D M - H

238

The coded message said that they were to break the bottle open! 'What an odd instruction,' remarked Dick, 'it would just waste the wine!' They thought there must be a reason for it, however, and so they hit the bottle against the rack. Much to their surprise, there wasn't any wine in the dark-coloured bottle but just a rolled-up map! 'Look, it's of around here,' said Julian and, since it seemed to have a lot more detail than their own maps, they decided to take it with them.

If you don't already have it, put the MAP CARD into your RUCKSACK. Now go to 269.

Trying to find his measuring tape in his rucksack, Dick took out his map to make it easier. Just as he had put it on the ground, however, a gust of wind came up and blew it into the water! They all started to run after it as it was blown further and further round the lake but the water finally soaked right into it and it began to sink. They were just about to return to where they had left their rucksacks when Julian noticed that they had come to a narrow wooden pier stretching over the reeds. And underneath it was hidden a small raft, moored to one of the supports! Dick was sent back to fetch their rucksacks while the others eagerly began to untie it!

If you have it, remove the MAP CARD from your RUCKSACK. Now go to 95.

Julian began stripping to his shorts ready to dive down to the boat but there was suddenly a loud splash as Timmy jumped in ahead of him! 'I hope he'll be all right,' said Julian as they watched him swim towards the boat's stern through the water. After a long anxious wait, though, he finally emerged – with a bag full of diamond necklaces in his mouth! 'Gosh, aren't they beautiful,' exclaimed Anne as they poured them on to the raft, 'they must be worth a fortune!' *Go to 45.*

The sergeant suddenly realised that it wasn't quite as safe at the front of the helicopter because of the open part, however, and so he decided he had better sit there himself while the children went in the back. 'We don't want any of you falling out, do we?' he chuckled over his shoulder as he fastened his seat-belt. The helicopter was soon whirring across the countryside but it had grown so dark that the pilot was becoming worried that he might have flown a bit off course. The sergeant could just make out the silhouette of a tall boundary stone on a hill below and he asked the children to look it up on their maps to check where they were.

Use your MAP CARD to find which square the boundary stone is in – then follow the instruction. If you don't have one, you'll have to guess which instruction to follow.

If you think A3	go to 230
If you think A4	go to 159
If you think B4	go to 211

242

George's map seemed to be right at the bottom of her rucksack and she lifted out her codebook to make it easier to find. Just at that moment, though, a bee started buzzing near her and she was so scared of being stung that she couldn't help throwing the codebook into the air. It went straight into the river! Although they managed to fish it out again, the pages were so wet that they decided just to leave it behind. 'Well, I would rather lose my codebook than have a bad sting!' George said moodily as they continued on their way.

If you have it, remove the CODEBOOK CARD from your RUCKSACK. Now go to 19.

They were still trying to decide whose suggestion to follow when they heard some voices calling them. Looking round, they saw that it was a couple of hikers at the bottom of the hill. 'Are you looking for somewhere?' they shouted. 'If so, maybe we can help.' Julian asked if they knew the way to Sinister Lake and they said that it was in the same direction as the distant radio mast. But as hard as they peered, the children weren't able to spot it. 'Perhaps it will be easier with our binoculars,' said George, beginning to open her rucksack for them.

Use your BINOCULARS CARD to try and find the radio mast by placing exactly over the shape below – then follow the instruction. If you don't have one, go to 205 instead.

G O A O   S   N   Z   G O ⅔ T N R O
T   O H ! O   R N   N   E % E E   C
T   F N   II R   E £ ꓷ I V   E   N   E
S   E ! E   I   S   G   X   H   E O   T

Focusing the binoculars on the trees, however, Dick saw that there was nothing there. 'I must have just imagined it,' he apologised. 'For a moment I thought there might be someone coming towards the house!' He was just turning away from the window when he noticed a small book hidden under the dust on the ledge. 'Look, it's a codebook,' he exclaimed, brushing it clean. 'It must have belonged to one of the people who used to live here!'

If you don't already have it, put the CODEBOOK CARD into your RUCKSACK. Now go to 56.

245

As soon as they had found the old ruin on their maps, Julian said that they had better get on with searching the cellar. 'That person who rang was obviously expecting someone else to be here,' he said, as he quickly led the way down the dark steps. 'So we might not have much time before they arrive!' *Go to 269.*

246

'Now, don't any one move about too much,' Dick warned as he paddled the raft further and further away from the bank, 'or you'll make us capsize!' A few seconds later, though, George seemed to forget about the warning because she suddenly jumped to her knees in excitement. 'Look at those ducks over there,' she said, pointing some distance to her right, 'I'm sure that one in the middle isn't real!' The others asked why anyone should possibly want to put an artificial duck there but she said it might be a secret marker for the jewels! 'Well, so I don't paddle all that way for nothing,' Dick told her, 'I suggest you have a better look at it first through your binoculars.'

Use your BINOCULARS CARD to see whether the duck is real or not by placing exactly over the shape below – then follow the instruction. If you don't have one, go to 290 instead.

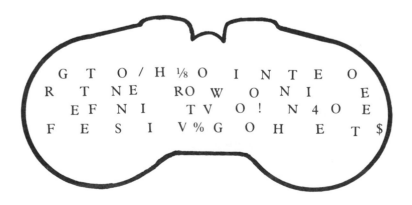

They all quietly watched as the two people came right up to the lake and started walking round the edge, obviously looking for the raft. 'We'll wait until they get a bit closer,' the sergeant whispered to his men, 'and then we'll jump out with our handcuffs!' The Five tried to see what the two people looked like but they were still just a bit too far away. But they gradually came nearer and they could hear one of them laughing at how clever the prisoner had been. The Five felt their hearts begin to pound as the laughter became clearer and clearer. Any second now, they would be able to see who the people were . . .

Use your CODEBOOK CARD to find out by decoding the answer below. If you don't have one, go to 135 instead.

When they tried to work out the secret message, however, they found that it was in a different code to the one in their books. 'What a nuisance!' exclaimed Julian as he put his codebook away again but then he suddenly noticed an old windmill not far to their right. 'Let's walk towards that,' he suggested, 'and see if we can climb to the top. The lake might well be visible from up there!' They were in such a hurry to get to the windmill, however, that Anne tripped on a molehill and went crashing to the ground. Fortunately, she wasn't hurt, but when she checked the contents of her rucksack she found that her binoculars were broken.

If you have it, remove the BINOCULARS CARD from your RUCKSACK. Now go to 36.

249

While they were looking for their codebooks, however, the tobacco tin slipped out of Julian's hand and rolled down the bank into the river! Julian tucked up his sleeve to try and reach it but the water was deeper than it looked. 'We'll just have to leave it,' he said as he dried his hand on the grass. The next thing they knew, though, something else was rolling into the water. It was Julian's measuring tape, which must have fallen out of his rucksack as he was putting it on again! They were just going to have to leave that as well!

If you have it, remove the MEASURE CARD from your RUCKSACK. Now go to 233.

250

'*JEWELS – ARE – HIDDEN – AT – SINISTER – LAKE,*' they all said out loud as they gradually worked the message out. They excitedly put their codebooks away again, realising that this must have been written by the same person as handed Dick that mysterious note! 'He probably wrote it in case he was caught before the note was delivered,' guessed Julian as they continued along the river bank. ***Go to 19.***

They had just found the start of the track when Dick suddenly slipped down the brook's muddy bank! Luckily, he just managed to stop himself before he got his foot wet but it meant letting go of his lunchbox. 'Oh no, it's gone into the water!' he cried to the others. 'Quick, do something before it sinks!' They all looked for a stick to try and hook it out but, by the time they had found one, there were just a few bubbles on the surface of the water. The lunchbox had gone right to the bottom!

Take one PICNIC CARD from your LUNCHBOX. Now go to 24.

As soon as Dick had jumped the brook, he stretched out his hand to help the others across. They were wondering which direction to go next for the lake when Anne suddenly noticed some wild ducks in the sky. 'They're almost certainly heading for the lake themselves,' she said, knowing how they liked large areas of water, 'and so all we have to do is see where they land!' But the ducks became smaller and smaller, making it difficult to work out which way they were flying. 'I know,' said Julian, suddenly starting to open his rucksack, 'let's look at them through our binoculars!'

Use your BINOCULARS CARD to follow the ducks' route by placing exactly over the shape below. If you don't have one, go to 194 instead.

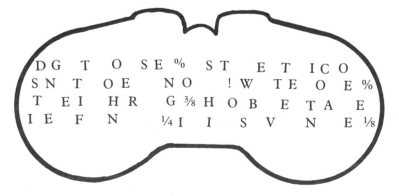

```
D G  T   O  S E  %   S T   E   T   I C O
S N  T   O E     N O     ! W   T E   O   E  %
T  E I   H R   G ⅜ H  O B   E   T A   E
I E   F  N    ¼ I   I   S   V    N    E  ⅛
```

Dick not only took out his codebook – but also his bottle of ginger beer. He thought he might as well have a drink while decoding the message! They had only just worked out the first word, however, when the bottle suddenly slipped from his hand and smashed on the stone. 'Now look what you've done,' George snapped at him crossly, '– your ginger beer's washed all the message away!' It was only when they had reached the other end of the stepping-stones, ten minutes later, that the others were prepared to talk to him again!

Take one PICNIC CARD from your LUNCHBOX. Now go to 91.

They were about to decode the chalked message when they suddenly realised that it had disappeared. 'I don't understand it,' remarked Julian, scratching his head, 'it was definitely this top step that it was on!' As he looked round, however, he noticed that there were chalky paw-marks all over the floor. 'So that's it,' he exclaimed, 'Timmy must have stood on the message!' They were about to tell him off when Dick noticed that there were one or two drops of liquid as well 'Oh no,' cried Anne, 'they're coming from the corner of my lunchbox. I couldn't have tightened the top of my bottle of ginger beer properly!'

Take one PICNIC CARD from your LUNCHBOX. Now go to 56.

255

'Okay, we'll agree on your idea, Dick,' the others said, since there wasn't really time to argue. So he led them through the trees and towards a ridge in the distance. 'I'm sure the village is over in that direction!' he told them. But he was later wondering whether it was the right way after all and he started looking for something they could identify on their maps. 'How about that large area of marshland over there?' asked Anne, and she slipped off her rucksack so she could take her map out.

Use your MAP CARD to find which square the marshland is in – then follow the instruction. If you don't have one, you'll have to guess which instruction to follow.

If you think D3	go to 319
If you think E3	go to 30
If you think D2	go to 158

256

Finding her binoculars just before the others, George quickly passed them over to Julian. 'Thanks,' he said and immediately started to focus them on the patch of blue below. 'Yes, it *is* the lake,' he exclaimed, '– I can even see our raft at the edge!' As the helicopter prepared to make its landing, Anne suddenly felt a small book by her feet. 'Why, it's a codebook!' remarked the sergeant. 'It must have fallen out of that prisoner's pocket when we were flying him back to the prison!'

If you don't already have it, put the CODEBOOK CARD into your RUCKSACK. Now go to 110.

257

They were still searching for their maps when Anne suddenly started laughing. 'How silly we all are,' she exclaimed, pointing to a painted sign at the far end of the green, '– look, the inn is just over there!' The others started laughing too, refastening their rucksacks before hurrying across to the inn. 'That gardener probably thought we were mad needing maps just to find our way to the other side,' Dick chuckled as he went. ***Go to 111.***

258

Anne's face lit up with excitement as the stile suddenly became visible ahead. 'I love walking over stiles,' she said eagerly. 'They're much more fun than going through gates!' The only one who didn't seem to agree was George. 'It might be fun for us humans,' she said, 'but what about poor Timmy? He always seems to get stuck half way over!' ***Go to 305.***

259

They decided that Julian had better go first to make sure the stepping-stones would take their weight. As long as the stones managed to support him – the heaviest – then they should be able to support everyone else! They at last reached the final stone, each jumping off on to firm ground again. Just before it was his turn to jump, though, Dick had a closer look at the stone. 'Hey, there's a message on it!' he exclaimed and he began to read it to the others. *'FOR SECRET HIDING PLACE,'* he read, *'GO 50 METRES IN LINE WITH THESE LAST TWO STONES.'*

So they quickly looked for their measuring tapes, anxious to see where this hiding place was!

*Use your **MEASURE CARD** to measure the 50 metres yourself – then follow the instruction there. If you don't have one, you'll have to guess which instruction to follow.*

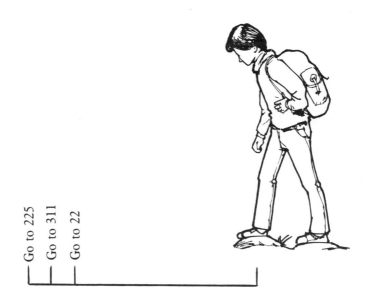

Go to 225

Go to 311

Go to 22

260

Their maps showed that the prison was only just over a mile from the lake and so they knew they must be very close now. 'If the lake is so near to the prison,' Dick said thoughtfully, 'I wonder why the prisoner didn't go straight there to pick up the jewels himself. It would seem a lot quicker than going all the way into the village to tell someone else!' Julian replied that it must be because the jewels were in a very difficult hiding place and it would have taken too much time to get them. ***Go to 79.***

261

They were just taking their binoculars out when a shaft of light came through one of the upper floor windows, revealing what the mysterious outline was. 'Look, it's just a suit of armour!' laughed Dick. 'See, Anne, we told you there was no one there!' Anne didn't really mind being teased about it, though, deciding she would much prefer that to finding it *had* been a real person! ***Go to 104.***

262

Timmy eventually offered to go down the cellar steps first, suddenly realising there might be some rats he could chase! The others all stayed close behind him as he finally reached the cold stone floor at the bottom and led the way through the wine racks. They hadn't gone far when George heard something rattle at her feet. 'Look, it's a box of matches,' she said and she lit one so they could see where they were going. Most of the wine racks were empty but they came to one with a bottle still there. Holding a match to the label, they saw that someone had written a coded message across it! 'Quick, let's take out our codebooks!' said Anne excitedly.

Use your CODEBOOK CARD to find out what the message

said by decoding the instruction below. If you don't have one, go to 278 instead.

263
Finally finding his binoculars, Julian directed them up the stairs until he reached the landing at the top. 'It's not much clearer than it was before,' he said, now moving the binoculars from one side to the other, 'but it *seems* all right up there!' So they cautiously started to climb the stairs, at last arriving at the landing. 'Right, let's go and explore some of the rooms,' said Dick a little nervously. ***Go to 117.***

264
Just as George was about to open her binoculars, however, she heard the bark again. In fact, it was repeated every five seconds and so they started to follow it. 'Look, there he is!' cried Dick, finally spotting Timmy some way to their left. He was standing at the side of the railway line and the others wondered why he had wanted to

bring them there. Then Julian realised. 'Of course,' he exclaimed, 'this must be the railway line that runs to the village. So all we have to do is follow it!' Partly because she was so pleased to find him again and partly because he was so clever, George gave Timmy a large slice of her cake!

Take one PICNIC CARD from your LUNCHBOX. Now go to 276.

265

The helicopter suddenly made a sharp turn, causing Julian to drop his lunchbox. Just as he was about to pick it up, the helicopter then did a sudden dip and it slid towards the open part at the front! 'Quick, someone do something!' he cried but it was too late. His lunchbox had fallen out and was now fast on its way to the ground!

Take one PICNIC CARD from your LUNCHBOX. Now go to 86.

266

They hadn't followed Anne far along the river-bank when she suddenly stopped to look at the bulrushes. One of them had a piece of ribbon tied to it! 'Look, there's a message written on it,' she exclaimed as she bent a little closer. 'It's addressed to someone called Reg and says that the binoculars are hidden one hundred paces further along!' Not surprisingly, The Five were soon counting out the hundred paces themselves!

Use your MEASURE CARD to measure the 100 paces from the

*bulrush – then follow the instruction there. If you don't have one in your **RUCKSACK** you'll have to guess which instruction to follow.*

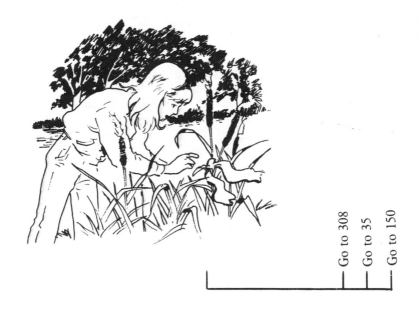

Go to 308

Go to 35

Go to 150

267

'*TO GET TO SINISTER LAKE,*' Julian read out as they decoded the rest of the message, '*MAKE YOUR WAY TO THE OLD WINDMILL AND CLIMB UP.*' To begin with, it didn't seem to make any more sense than when it was in code but then Anne suddenly noticed an old windmill not far to their right. 'The message must mean that you can see Sinister Lake from the top,' she said as they set off towards it. On their way, they all wondered who had written the secret message. Then Dick realised that it was in exactly the same handwriting as the mysterious note he had received at the farmhouse. It must have been the escaped prisoner again! *Go to 36.*

268

Just as they were about to open their maps, however, they heard someone shouting at them from the observation hut. 'Shoo, go away, or you'll frighten the birds!' the angry voice said. So they did as they were told, continuing on their way, but they thought the person could have been a lot more polite about it. 'Besides, he probably frightened them much more by his shouting,' Dick remarked sulkily. He would have been even more sulky if he had known that, in his hurry to put his map away again, he had dropped his codebook!

*If you have one, remove the **CODEBOOK CARD** from your **RUCKSACK**. Now go to 91.*

269

Dick suddenly ordered them all to be quiet, thinking he heard footsteps above! 'Yes, there they are again,' he whispered anxiously '– someone must have come into the house!' In fact, it must have been two people because they now heard one of them talking. 'Let's go back up the stairs and try and hear what he's saying,' suggested Julian. The person's voice wasn't all that clear but he said something about the jewels being hidden in the lake and that he would come back and look for them after dark in case there was anybody about. Then he added that he had left the equipment sixty metres from the old sundial in the house's grounds. It wasn't much longer before the two strangers left and The Five were able to creep out into the kitchen again. 'Let's go and measure sixty metres from the sundial ourselves,' said Julian breathlessly, 'and see what equipment they are talking about!'

Use your MEASURE CARD to measure the 60 metres from the sundial – then follow the instruction there. If you don't have one, you'll have to guess which instruction to follow.

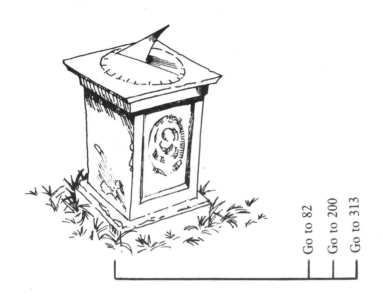

Go to 82
Go to 200
Go to 313

270

They were still searching for their binoculars when there was suddenly a strong gust of wind across the lake. The next thing they knew, a small raft appeared out of the reeds a little further round, drifting towards the middle! 'The wind must have blown it out of its hiding place,' said Julian and they all quickly looked for a long stick to try and hook it back to the edge. By the time they had found one, however, it had gone too far out. They were just wondering what they were going to do about it when there was an almighty splash as

Timmy leapt into the water! Swimming up to the raft, he started to push it back with his nose. 'Clever boy, Timmy!' they all cheered as he finally steered it into the reeds, and George gave him a big slice of her cake as a reward.

Take one PICNIC CARD from your LUNCHBOX. Now go to 57.

271

They were still trying to find their measuring tapes when Julian suddenly realised something. The measuring could only be done if someone was at either end of the tape – but that wouldn't be possible without two rafts! So they decided they would just have to guess the fifty metres. George offered round some of her cake on the way in case anyone was getting hungry again. *She* certainly was!

Take one PICNIC CARD from your LUNCHBOX. Now go to 97.

272

'You need to go over that way!' Julian told the pilot, pointing to the moorland area in the distance. The helicopter flew higher and higher, however, and he was having trouble identifying the lake. He couldn't be sure whether it was that patch of blue down there or not! So he turned round to the others, asking to borrow a pair of their binoculars.

Use your BINOCULARS CARD to help Julian spot the lake by placing exactly over the shape below – then follow the instruction. If you don't have one, go to 293 instead.

```
    G  TE  O  S  E   S  E  F  T  T  SO  O
  2 O    T    O    W    O @        O  S  NO         E
    F   SE        I        VXQE    N    V      W      E
    F  !    S      E    I  V £      GT    X      E N          9
```

273

The man said that they didn't need their measuring tapes, however, for he would show them the gate himself. Although it would mean delaying him for a few minutes, he said he really didn't mind since it was such a lovely day. So he turned round and started walking back again, telling them about some of the butterflies he had caught that morning. 'Anyway, there's the gate!' he said after a short while, pointing to a small gap in the hedge. 'When you've gone through, just keep walking across the fields for another half mile or so.' *Go to 36.*

274

'Yes, it *is* that man and woman,' George exclaimed as she focused her binoculars on them, 'I can see his horrible scowling face!' They seemed to be busy talking to each other but it wasn't much longer before they stood up and walked away. 'Right – now they've gone, let's head in that direction ourselves,' said Julian. 'We ought to be back where we were before long!' *Go to 64.*

275

They had only measured twenty of the thirty metres when Dick suddenly gave a loud gasp. 'Everybody stay exactly where they are!' he ordered, feeling cautiously round with his foot. 'There's just an empty space in front!' If they had gone a couple of centimetres more, they would have fallen right through to the ground floor! 'That note must have been put there as a trap for intruders,' said Julian as they carefully backed off. 'I suppose the idea was that you would be so busy measuring that you wouldn't realise the floor suddenly ended until it was too late!' To help them all recover from this nasty shock, Anne offered round her ginger beer.

Take one PICNIC CARD from your LUNCHBOX. Now go to 56.

276

They had been following the railway line for nearly an hour now and the daylight was rapidly fading. 'I hope we reach the village station soon,' said Julian, 'or we might not be able to get back to the lake in time!' Of course, they not only had to reach the railway station but there was also the walk from there to the police station. So they would know which end of the village the railway station was, Julian suggested they stop a moment to look it up on their maps.

Use your MAP CARD to find which square the railway station is in – then follow the instruction. If you don't have one, you'll have to guess which instruction to follow.

If you think A1	go to 109
If you think A2	go to 220
If you think B2	go to 180

'Well, we can't wait here all day!' said Dick, and so he eventually led the way up the stairs himself. Reaching the top, they noticed a small window at the far end of the landing and they felt their way towards it so they could see better. 'You get a good view of the grounds from here,' commented Dick, peering out – but then his voice suddenly went strange. He thought he noticed someone move amongst the trees! 'Quick, hand me a pair of binoculars!' he said, not quite able to see clearly enough.

Use your BINOCULARS CARD to get a better look at the trees by placing exactly over the shape below – then follow the instruction. If you don't have one, go to 218 instead.

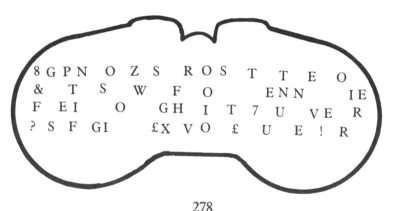

278

By the time they had found their codebooks, however, they were down to their last match. 'Quick, do something before it goes out!' George cried urgently as the flame burnt nearer and nearer to her fingers. Julian hurriedly handed her a sheet of paper from his rucksack and she was just able to light it in time. But then he suddenly realised what the paper was! 'Oh no,' he exclaimed as he watched it flare up, 'that was my map!' They all tried to put it out again but there was quite a draught down there and the map was soon reduced to ash.

If you have one, remove the MAP CARD from your rucksack. Now go to 269.

To keep one end of the measuring tape at the float, Dick had the clever idea of hooking it over the pointed bit at the top. Julian then started to paddle in the direction of the tree, Anne gradually feeding more and more of the tape out from the spool. Suddenly, though, Julian paddled a bit too hard and the top of the float broke off! 'We'll just have to try and do without the measuring tape,' said Anne as she reeled it in again. In fact, they had only gone a little further when she suddenly pointed at something under the murky water. 'Look, it's a sunken rowing-boat,' she cried excitedly, 'and I can just see a red polythene bag inside. It must be the jewels!' To celebrate, George let everyone have a drink of her ginger beer!

Take one PICNIC CARD from your LUNCHBOX. Now go to 240. (Remember: when there are no picnic cards left in your lunchbox, the game is over and you must start again.)

Just at that moment, though, they heard two pairs of footsteps coming towards the lake and someone talking. 'Quick, hide!' whispered the sergeant and they all rushed for cover behind a nearby group of trees. In fact, they were in such a panic about it that George tripped over one of the tree's roots, dropping her lunchbox. Fortunately, she didn't make too much of a noise but she could tell from the slight tinkle inside her lunchbox that her bottle of ginger beer had broken!

Take one PICNIC CARD from your LUNCHBOX. Now go to 247. (Remember: when there are no picnic cards left in your lunchbox, the game is over and you must start again.)

'I can't see the lake anywhere,' said Julian as he focused his binoculars. Moving them round a bit, however, he suddenly spotted an old windmill on a nearby hill and he suggested that they try searching for the lake again from there. 'As long as it's not locked up,' he said as he led the way, 'we should be able to climb right to the top!' There was still another couple of fields to cross when something became wrapped around Anne's feet. 'Look, it's a measuring tape!' she remarked when she had finally managed to unravel it all. 'Since the owner's hardly likely to find it again, let's take it with us as a spare!'

If you don't already have it, put the MEASURE CARD into your RUCKSACK. Now go to 36.

'All this counting is making me thirsty,' said Dick when there were still forty paces to go – and so he ordered them all to stay exactly where they were while he had a sip of his ginger beer! 'Right, you can start counting again!' he chuckled when he had put his bottle back in his lunchbox. Finally, reaching the last of the paces, they saw that there was a large rock in the middle of the brook at this point. 'It must have been put there to form a stepping-stone,' said Julian and, one by one, they all used it to get across.

Take one PICNIC CARD from your LUNCHBOX. Now go to 79.

They were just about to explore further along the first floor when Julian's rucksack suddenly fell off his back! 'One of the straps must have come loose,' he said as he picked it up again. He anxiously felt around inside to make sure his binoculars weren't damaged. 'Oh no,' he said as he cut his finger on a piece of sharp glass, 'it looks like one of the lenses has broken!'

If you have it, remove the BINOCULARS CARD from your RUCKSACK. Now go to 117.

Julian offered to do the paddling, kneeling at the front of the raft and repeatedly pulling the branch through the water. It wasn't as good as a proper oar but it wasn't bad! He hadn't paddled them far when George noticed a small brown object floating on the surface some distance to their right. 'I wonder if that's got something to do with the jewels?' she asked excitedly. 'Perhaps it's a marker or something!' Julian started to paddle towards it to find out but George just couldn't wait, deciding to take a look through her binoculars right away! She quickly searched her rucksack for them.

Use your BINOCULARS CARD to get a better look at the object by placing exactly over the shape below – then follow the instruction. If you don't have one, go to 84 instead.

'Yes, it *is* the village,' George said with delight as she looked through her binoculars, 'I can just make out the station!' In fact, following the line back from the station, she noticed that it ran quite close to the bottom of their hill. So all they had to do was follow it! As they were hurrying towards the line, Julian suddenly spotted a circular leather case in the grass. 'Look, it's a measuring tape!' he exclaimed, and he decided to take it with him to hand in at the police station.

If you don't already have it, put the MEASURE CARD into your RUCKSACK. Now go to 276.

286
Just as George was handing her binoculars to Dick, however, the moon came out and started reflecting on something large and round below. 'It must be the lake!' cried Dick excitedly. 'Only water would shine that brightly!' As the helicopter swooped down towards it, George munched on a slice of her cake so her ears wouldn't pop!

Take one PICNIC CARD from your LUNCHBOX. Now go to 110.

287
They hadn't been following Julian's choice of route far when the ground started to become a little wet. 'I don't understand,' said Dick, scratching his head, 'there hasn't been a drop of rain all day!' The ground grew more and more soggy, though, and they suddenly

realised they had walked right into the middle of a large mire. 'Quick, start going back,' Julian shouted to the others, 'or we might get sucked under!' Fortunately, they finally managed to reach hard ground again and they were a lot more careful where they trod this time. As they walked round the mire's edge, Julian suggested they look it up on their maps to find out roughly where they were.

Use your MAP CARD to find which square the mire is in – then follow the instruction. If you don't have one, you'll have to guess which instruction to follow.

If you think E3	go to 234
If you think D3	go to 301
If you think D4	go to 64

288

Anne eventually offered to walk down the steps first, thinking it might make one of the others feel guilty and insist on taking her place. But, unfortunately, it didn't and so she just had to go ahead! The cellar was even darker than the rest of the house but she suddenly put her hand on a candle lying on a shelf. And next to it there was a box of matches! Lighting the candle, she saw that someone had chalked a message on the cellar roof. 'It's just a bit too high up to read,' said George disappointedly but then she remembered that they had binoculars with them!

Use your BINOCULARS CARD to try and read the message by

placing exactly over the shape below – then follow the instruction. If you don't have one, go to 208 instead.

289

While they were looking for their codebooks, Timmy suddenly went wandering off towards a mass of reeds a little further round the lake. 'What is it, Timmy?' they all asked impatiently as he started to bark back at them. They were still trying to find their codebooks and they thought he had just discovered a family of ducks or something. His barks became much more insistent, though, and then they noticed that he had the end of a piece of rope in his mouth! Forgetting about their codebooks for a moment, they all ran up to him to see what was at the other end of the rope. It was a small raft, hidden amongst the reeds! As a reward, George gave him a large slice of her cake!

Take one PICNIC CARD from your LUNCHBOX. Now go to 57.

290

George was still searching for her binoculars when Julian thought of a much quicker way of finding out if the duck was real or not. He crumbled up a slice of his cake and threw all the pieces into the water. One by one, the ducks came flying towards them to investigate. The duck that George had been talking about looked as if it was going to be the only one to stay – but then it, too, flapped in their direction! 'Well, it doesn't look very artificial to me,' Julian chuckled, deciding it was worth a piece of his cake just to see George's embarrassment!

Take one PICNIC CARD from your LUNCHBOX. Now go to 120.

291

They had only counted half a dozen or so of the paces when Julian insisted that they go back again. 'I'm sure we started from the wrong place,' he said. 'I seem to remember the branch was lying much nearer to the trees when Dick picked it up.' On returning to their starting point, however, they saw that there was still the impression of the branch in the grass and so it must have been the right place after all! 'Right, let's begin the counting again!' sighed the others with a bit of a chuckle. *Go to 318.*

292

Moving her binoculars round, George suddenly spotted the train in the distance and she then started to trace the line back. 'It must run somewhere behind that ridge over there,' she said, pointing a mile or so to their left. So they quickly set off towards the ridge, discovering that the line *did* run behind it! 'All we have to do now is keep following it until we reach the village!' Julian said gleefully. *Go to 276.*

293

They had all left their rucksacks right at the back of the helicopter, however, and it was impossible to get to them for their binoculars. 'Never mind,' said the pilot, 'I'll try flying a bit lower.' As the ground came closer and closer below, Julian at last spotted the lake. 'There it is – a little to the left!' he exclaimed and the pilot prepared to land. *Go to 110.*

294

With the help of their measuring tapes, they quickly found the little gate and they all went through to the field on the other side. 'Look, there's the windmill!' Anne exclaimed, soon spotting its huge white sails ahead. As they were running towards it, however, Timmy suddenly stopped to investigate something in the grass. Taking it from him, George saw that it was a book with strange symbols inside. 'Hey, it's a codebook!' she shouted to the others. Although they each had a codebook with them, they decided to take this one along as well in case it was a different type.

If you don't already have it, put the CODEBOOK CARD into your RUCKSACK. Now go to 36.

295

'Make sure you have a good run-up,' Julian called back to the others when he had jumped to the other side of the brook. They all just managed to make it, Julian giving them a hand so they didn't fall back. 'Now where do we go?' asked Dick, but then he suddenly noticed someone washing pans further along the brook. 'Look, it's a camper,' he said. 'Let's ask him!' After saying hello to the camper, they told him that they were looking for Sinister Lake. The man advised them to keep walking along the brook for another 170 paces and then they would find the start of a small sheep-track which would take them most of the way there.

*Use your **MEASURE CARD** to measure the 170 paces – then follow the instruction there. If you don't have one, you'll have to guess which instruction to follow.*

Go to 77

Go to 251

Go to 24

296

They were still looking for their binoculars in their rucksacks when Julian suddenly noticed an old windmill just across the next field. 'We'd get a much better view from the top of there,' he told the others excitedly. So they quickly fastened their rucksacks up again, hurrying in the mill's direction. They only hoped that they could still get in and that it hadn't been locked up! ***Go to 36.***

'Oh, I'm sure there's nothing to be scared of!' said Julian bravely after a while and he started to lead the way up the stairs himself. They had just reached the top when Dick noticed a piece of paper stuck to the banister with a drawing pin! He pulled the pin out, thinking there might be some sort of message written on the paper. There was! 'It says that we are to walk thirty metres to the right,' he told the others excitedly. They wasted no time in looking for their measuring tapes!

Use your MEASURE CARD to measure the 30 metres – then follow the instruction there. If you don't have one, you'll have to guess which instruction to follow.

Go to 275

Go to 312

Go to 166

Focusing her binoculars on the duck, George suddenly gave a shout of delight. 'I was right – it isn't real,' she exclaimed. 'I can see the streaks of paint!' So Dick hurriedly started paddling towards it. Although the duck *was* an artificial one, however, they couldn't see any sign of the jewels underneath. 'Well, it must have been put here for *some* reason,' said George and then she noticed that there was a small slit along its back. Pressing her eye against it, she could just see a folded sheet of paper inside. 'It might be instructions!' she said breathlessly and tipped the duck upside down. Although the map that fell out wasn't quite as exciting as they had hoped, it could still come in useful as a spare!

If you don't already have it, put the MAP CARD into your RUCKSACK. Now go to 120.

299

Since he was the only one who *didn't* feel a bit scared, Timmy went through the door first. 'Ooh, isn't it dark?' said Anne as she made sure she kept a hand on Timmy's tail. It was very dusty too – as if the place hadn't been used for years and years! They hadn't gone far when Julian felt something lumpy under his foot. 'You don't think it's a dead rat?' asked George anxiously but Julian said it felt more like a bag of some sort. So he kicked it towards where a shaft of light shone on the floor from a small window. Seeing that it *was* a bag, he opened it up. 'Look, it's full of weird tools – crowbars, and wire-cutters and things!' he exclaimed. They wondered what they were for but then Julian noticed a large coded message on the bottom of the bag. 'Perhaps that will explain!' he said, hurriedly looking for his codebook.

Use your CODEBOOK CARD to find out what the message

said by decoding the instruction below. If you don't have one, go to 217 instead.

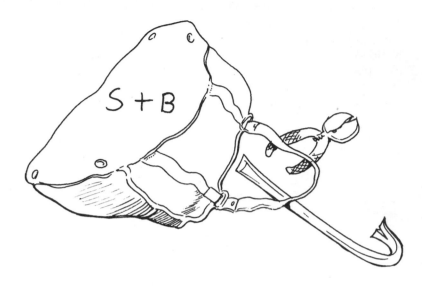

300

Hooking the end of the measuring tape over the point of the float, they then started paddling the raft in the direction of the tree. 'There's only ten more metres to go,' said Dick as he carefully fed the tape out from the spool. He was just about to tell them that they had reached the sixty-metre mark when Anne gave an excited shout. 'Look, down there!' she cried, pointing into the murky water. 'There's a sunken rowing-boat with a large polythene bag inside. It must be the jewels!' *Go to 240.*

They had only gone a few steps more when Dick stopped to take off his shoes. Walking through the mire had made his socks soaking wet and he decided to change them for a spare pair he had put in his rucksack. They were right at the bottom, however, and it meant taking everything else out to find them. When he repacked, he overlooked his codebook and it was left behind in the grass!

If you have it, remove the **CODEBOOK CARD** *from your* **RUCKSACK.** *Now go to 64.*

The coded message said that the jewels were hidden in the deepest part of the lake! 'That will probably be in the middle somewhere,' said Julian and so he told George to start paddling again. She dipped the branch into the water even faster this time, anxious to get there as quickly as possible. 'Not too madly,' Dick had to warn her, 'or you'll have us capsizing!' *Go to 120.*

They were still waiting for someone to offer to go down the cellar steps first when there was a sudden ringing noise from the other end of the kitchen! 'It sounds like a phone,' said Dick with surprise and, feeling their way towards the ringing, they found that it was! Curiously picking it up, Julian heard a rough-sounding voice at the other end. 'I just wanted to make sure you found the place all right, Richie,' it growled before Julian could say anything. 'When you've got the jewels, I'll meet you at the old ruin.' As soon as the voice had rung off, Julian told the others to look up the old ruin on their maps so they could tell the police about it later on.

Use your MAP CARD to find which square the old ruin is in – then follow the instruction. If you don't have one, you'll have to guess which instruction to follow.

If you think A3	go to 245
If you think B2	go to 116
If you think C3	go to 314

304

They had only walked a few hundred metres from the windmill when they all suddenly jumped at a loud creaking noise from behind. 'Ooh, w-w-what's that?' asked Anne, not daring to turn round. When they finally looked round, however, they started laughing at how silly they were. 'It's just the windmill's sails being turned by a gust of wind!' Dick chuckled. *Go to 113.*

Reaching the stile, they all got ready to climb over. It was quite difficult with their rucksacks on and it didn't prove as much fun as they expected. 'Oh, look out!' they all cried as Anne caught her foot at the top but it was too late – she went tumbling to the ground. Luckily, she only had a slight graze on her elbow but when she stood up again she heard a rattling noise from her rucksack. Looking inside, she found that it was exactly as she had feared – her binoculars were broken!

If you have it, remove the BINOCULARS CARD from your RUCKSACK. Now go to 224.

They were in the middle of counting the 140 paces when they all heard a loud whirring noise above. Looking up, they saw that it was a police helicopter. 'They must be searching for the escaped prisoner,' said Anne. 'I hope he's not anywhere near here!' The helicopter soon moved away but they had been so disturbed by it that they couldn't remember how many paces they had counted. 'We'll just have to start again!' sighed Julian. *Go to 123.*

They were just about to follow the footpath across the fields, when Dick noticed his lunchbox had changed colour! Then he realised what had happened. 'Oh no,' he cried, 'I must have picked up the fisherman's bait box by mistake!' So he hurried back to exchange them but, when he inspected his lunchbox, he saw that some of his sandwiches were missing. 'I'm afraid I made a mistake as well,' the fisherman confessed with a chuckle. 'I absent-mindedly crumbled up two of your sandwiches for bait!' After they'd had a good laugh together about it, Dick hurried back to the footpath to catch the others up.

Take one PICNIC CARD from your LUNCHBOX. Now go to 163.

308

'I can't *see* any binoculars!' exclaimed George when they had reached a hundred paces. They searched all round the bulrushes and amongst the rocks. They even looked to see if they had been hidden in the river itself in a waterproof container. 'This person Reg must have already taken them,' said Julian and as they continued on their journey they discussed who he might be. 'You don't think it's the escaped prisoner and those binoculars were to help him find his way?' Dick asked with a sudden thrill. *Go to 19.*

309

'I don't see it's any of your business,' Julian told the man boldly, 'but if you must know we're heading for Sinister Lake.' To begin with, the man seemed angry at this but then he noticed Timmy growling at him and he suddenly became a lot more friendly. 'Oh, the only reason I asked,' he said with a thin smile, 'is that I thought I might be able to direct you. In actual fact, you're going the wrong way. There is a lake near here but it's called Willow Lake. Sinister Lake is in a completely different direction.' He pointed to a ridge on the horizon, saying the lake was just behind it, and he waved them a warm goodbye as they started the long trek towards it. *Go to 206.*

310

They were so busy talking, however, that they suddenly forgot what number they were up to! 'Was it pace eighty-four or eighty-five?' asked Dick, scratching his head. From the eager look on his face, Timmy seemed to know . . . but, of course, he was unable to tell them. So it looked as if there was nothing for it but just to start counting again from the beginning! ***Go to 282.***

311

While she was looking through her rucksack for her measuring tape, George suddenly realised that her map was missing. 'It must have dropped out somewhere!' she said and asked if they could go back and look for it. So they all went back across the stones and tried to follow the way they had come. But the map was nowhere to be seen and they finally made their way back towards the message about the hiding place. They had lost so much time, however, that Julian decided they had better forget about the measuring and just continue on their way.

If you have it, remove the MAP CARD from your RUCKSACK. Now go to 91.

They were just about to start measuring the thirty metres when they realised they didn't know where to measure from! It was meant to have been where the piece of paper was pinned to the banister but of course Dick had removed the paper in order to read it. Then Anne suddenly had an idea – they could feel for the pin-hole! 'Here it is,' exclaimed George after a few minutes of running her hands along the banister, '– now let's get back to the measuring!' *Go to 275.*

313

They were just about to go looking for the sundial, however, when Anne suggested they leave it a while in case those people hadn't quite left the area yet. The others agreed it was a good idea and so they waited a few minutes just inside the house's front door. 'Right, the coast should be absolutely clear now,' said Julian and they all stepped out into the open air again. *Go to 82.*

314

While she was searching for her map, however, Anne suddenly realised something. 'That person who rang was obviously expecting someone else to be here,' she told the others in a worried voice. 'So they could well be arriving any minute!' They therefore decided to forget about looking up their maps for the moment and return to the more important job of exploring the cellar. They all immediately made their way down the steps, now in too much of a hurry to be nervous! *Go to 269.*

315

They were still looking for the lake on their maps when Anne suddenly realised something. 'Oh, aren't I silly?' she remarked. 'A boathouse would be too small to be shown, anyway!' So they put their maps away again, deciding they would just have to go looking for a boathouse the hard way after all! It wasn't long, though, before they found one – hidden behind some weeping willows at the water's edge – and they all squeezed through the rotting door. Although there weren't any boats there, there *was* a small raft and they eagerly began to untie it. *Go to 57.*

316

While the others were searching for their binoculars, Dick suddenly noticed a railway line not far from the bottom of their hill. 'Hey, that must be the line that runs to the village,' he said excitedly, '– so you needn't bother about your binoculars because all we have to do is follow it!' He was in such a hurry to lead the way down to the line, however, that he suddenly tripped and started to roll over and over. Finally coming to a stop at the very bottom of the hill, he was relieved to find that his rucksack was still on his back. But he didn't realise that his measuring tape had fallen out!

If you have it, remove the MEASURE CARD from your RUCKSACK. Now go to 276.

317

George was just taking her binoculars out, however, when they heard a loud whistle from the train and they suddenly spotted it a mile or so to their left. Now they knew where the line was, they quickly made their way towards it, beginning to follow it into the village. They hadn't gone far when George said there must be another train approaching because she could hear a slight rumble. But then she suddenly realised that it was coming from Timmy's tummy! 'He must be hungry, poor thing!' she laughed as she gave him a slice of her cake.

Take one PICNIC CARD from your LUNCHBOX. Now go to 276.

318

When they finally reached one hundred paces, however, there were no binoculars to be seen. 'Someone must have already taken them,' said Julian. So they hurried back to the raft, deciding they would take it in turns to do the paddling. George was becoming so excited as they approached the middle of the lake that she couldn't help nibbling on a piece of her cake!

Take one PICNIC CARD from your LUNCHBOX. Now go to 97.

319

The daylight was rapidly fading, however, and their maps were difficult to see properly. 'How silly we were not to bring a torch!' remarked Anne as she squinted at the symbols, trying to make them out. Julian said if they took much longer about it, they probably wouldn't get back to the village until it was too late anyway. So they decided to put their maps away again and just hope this *was* the right way. Before they set off again, George had a quick drink of her ginger beer in case there wasn't time later on.

Take one PICNIC CARD from your LUNCHBOX. Now go to 59.

THE ENID BLYTON TRUST
FOR CHILDREN

We hope you have enjoyed the adventures of the children in this book. Please think for a moment about those children who are too ill to do the exciting things you and your friends do.

Help them by sending a donation, large or small, to the ENID BLYTON TRUST FOR CHILDREN. The Trust will use all your gifts to help children who are sick or handicapped and need to be made happy and comfortable.

Please send your postal orders or cheques to:

The Enid Blyton Trust For Children,
Lee House,
London Wall,
London EC2Y 5AS.

Thank you very much for your help.